Imagining Eden

Adrian Bean

Imagining
Eden

As It Was
and
How It Might Have Been
in the World of
The Panacea Society

BROWN
DOG
BOOKS

Published under licence by Brown Dog Books and
The Self-Publishing Partnership, 7 Green Park Station,
Bath BA1 1JB

www.selfpublishingpartnership.co.uk

ISBN printed book: 978-1-78545-316-8
ISBN e-book: 978-1-78545-317-5

Cover design by Andrew Prescott
Internal design by Andrew Easton

Printed and bound by CPI Group (UK) Ltd,
Croydon, CR04YY

Acknowledgements

———◄►◄◄►———

The illustration in chapter 2
is by Society member John Coghill.
All other illustrations, including the cover,
are by another member, John Rupert Waldron Tanner.
He had quite an imagination.
Many thanks to the Panacea Charitable Trust
for allowing me to use these illustrations
from the archives, and to Jill Brown
for the proof-reading.

Most of all, thanks to Gemma Papineau
for the editing,
but especially for her
bubbly enthusiasm, encouragement
and advice.
(Without whom this would not have been possible etc etc).

A BOX!

A misunderstood apostrophe

Gardens

Weird Voices

Secrets

A man with a moustache

More Secrets

A Boat Trip

Suffragettes

Pieces of Linen

A Snake *Diaries*

Petitions *Spooky Houses*

Apples

TEAPOTS!!

A Jackdaw

The Devil

THEOLOGY

Mysteries   A Roundabout

GOTHS

country dancing

HYMNS

The Jarrow March

Virtually no s*x at all

A Messiah   Paradise

Millenarianism

Ceremonies!   Cod Philosophy

Some FUN

People who could believe six impossible things before breakfast

Contents

Preamble   11

Gardens of Eden   13

The Boat - One Tuesday Afternoon 2015   16

Forever Six O'clock - 1874   18

The Full Mabel - How it all Started   20

Etholle - In The Beginning   24

The Full Mabel - A Very English Messiah   29

Etholle - Coming To Bedford   33

The Full Mabel - Strange People - Strange Ideas   38

Etholle - Singing For Zion   44

The Full Mabel - The Garden and The Healing   49

Etholle - Sitting At The Roundabout   52

The Full Mabel - The Box   56

Faces - 12 Albany Road Bedford Jan 1920   60

Etholle - One Way   62

DoG - 1920   72

The Full Mabel - The Flock Grows   75

At The Haven 2016   78

Etholle - Heavy People   81

A Fly. A Solitary Fly	*87*
Etholle - Witchfinders	*92*
Happy Families 1933	*100*
Ceremonials	*102*
16ᵗʰ October 1934	*106*
Etholle - Old Crones	*109*
Etholle - Thinking About Things I Don't Understand	*113*
Etholle - The Fun We Had	*119*
From Olga Hughes' Diary	*125*
Etholle - In Every Eden a Heartache	*130*
Etholle - Break-in 1975	*138*
Etholle - The Chosen 1975	*141*
Etholle - Saddos, Weirdos and Social Inadequates	*144*
Etholle - Dream - 1988	*152*
Gary - Thoughts From The Café	*156*
Lilith - Nothing At The End Of The Rainbow - 2017	*164*
Home with the Clancys - 2017	*171*
The End	*177*
Looking Through Dilys Barltrop's Eyes - October 1934	*179*

Preamble

"You may think I'm just a silly old fool who shouldn't be allowed to write nonsense like this and you may be right. But then again, you may be wrong. How DARE you say I'm a silly old fool who shouldn't be allowed to write nonsense like this. I'll have you know that I've as much right to write nonsense like this as you have. Maybe more so. And let that be an end to it!"

(BBC Radio Comedy programme, The Navy Lark)

"so long as a man rides his HOBBYHORSE peaceably and quietly along the king's highway, and neither compels you or me to get up behind him, pray, Sir, what have either you or I to do with it?"

(Laurence Sterne, Tristram Shandy)

"There is nothing new under the sun."

(Ecclesiastes 1.9)

Entertain, Educate, Inform.

(Early BBC mission/slogan)

I'm an amateur*.....but not too amateurish**

* " amateur"- a person who admires something. A devotee. A fan.

a person who engages in study, sport or other activity for pleasure rather than for financial benefit or professional reasons.

** " amateurish"- inept.

Gardens of Eden

Here's a challenge for you: Imagine what the Garden of Eden was like.

Go on, think about it...

Well.....

Some people in Cumbria are lucky enough to live in a place called Eden, some people in Cornwall work in Eden, and a Chelsea footballer IS Eden; but I bet your first thought was of the Eden in the Bible, where Adam and Eve lived in a beautiful place with exotic flowers and plants, no doubt with a pretty stream babbling along and pleasant-sounding birds stomping about in the trees. Probably it's somewhere tropical, with lots of colourful fruits and lush greenery. The sun will be shining, no changeable weather there I reckon. No of course not, because all is perfect and lovely. Meanwhile, at the back of your mind you know that things went wrong, for whatever reason, and the humans, or Satan, messed it all up. In your mind's eye you get a feeling about what Eden must have been like, just for a brief time rather than the permanent Eden that God perhaps intended. Eden, or Paradise, might be a permanent state, but it could be just a quick glimpse that you get from time to time.

We all have Perfect Moments of different kinds. You know those times, when all is right with the world, and everything in the garden is rosy, a moment or perhaps hours when things are first class, top hole, gold medal winning and cloudless. Days you'll remember all your life, you might say. Perfect Days.

Those perfect moments are very different from one person to another. It could be Howard Carter discovering Tut's tomb, or you getting a waggy welcome home from your dog, or scoring a goal at Wembley, or just getting a smile and a "hello" from a stranger in a strange town. They are all the same thing, getting a glimpse of what a heaven might feel like. Is there a Heaven? You'd like to think so, but ideas of Heaven can be strange. I remember years ago there was a Rubens exhibition somewhere in the Netherlands and someone had written in a comments book:

"My idea of Heaven: Massive Dutch Sluts." *(Reader, Don't Panic! There'll be no more coarseness in this book. It was ok in the Seventies)*.

The traditional view of Eden is the one shown by Bosch in "The Garden of Earthly Delights" which does show the idyllic Eden on one side, but it also shows Hell on the other side, after things went wrong and Satan had his say in things.

The Panaceans believed in a physical Garden of Eden which they wanted to recreate in the England of the twentieth century. They believed Jesus was going to return, to bring a new millennium of Peace and Heaven on Earth. Their lifestyle, beliefs and actions might seem to be out of a weird fairy story, but if we could have listened in to their conversations in the 1920's and 1930's I suspect we would also be struck, amongst other things, by their sheer sincerity and perhaps innocence. We might pity them for deluding themselves into living in a fantasy world, backed up by impressive Biblical authority but which was just wishful thinking. They failed but never gave up – Obsession never sleeps, just like rust. Yet without really trying as hard as they might, they had a world-wide impact, genuinely having an effect on people's lives and not, as some might think, being just an ornament of the age. Their leader Mabel Barltrop (a wonderful name, isn't it) had mental illnesses for much of her life, but she must undoubtedly have been a charismatic person, and the kind of leader that followers trusted so much that they might willingly "go over the top of the trenches" for her if ordered.

It wasn't a "cult" in the way that, for example, the "Exclusive Brethren" was/is/might be, waiting for "The Rapture," (although a few members might have been happy and dominant in that kind of environment). But if it was, then it was a very English cult.

She, they, believed they lived in an Eden; and you, we, might also have a bit of a yen for experiencing their fantastical castles in the air.

There are no voice recordings of Mabel. There are masses of

written records of the members and their activities, but as with all historical records, they can be open to different interpretations. There are diaries, statistics, reports and all of that jive, but none nail down what the individuals were really like when off guard or in chatterbox mode. So, just as they imagined their Eden, we can imagine what they did and how they thought in their self imposed prison/wonderland.

Some of the events and people mentioned in this book are genuine and even the strangest things might be true.The fictional bits are based on facts, but with a little imagination thrown in. Some comments are clearly my own opinions. Etholle is an imagined character. I think it's a lovely maverick name (pronounced ETHerly, rhyming with "breath") and I've only ever come across one lucky person with that particular feather in their cap. Mrs G and the Clancys are also imagined characters. I've tried to make the tone conversational and relaxed, and followed a famous writer's instructions on using simple words that normal people use (such as the honest down-to-earth "stay" rather than the posh and haughty "remain")...but I have tried to be a clever dick in some places – you'll notice them and tut tut. Words are important.

Also, for fun, I've made references to books, phrases and songs that an intelligent sort like me born in 1953 finds interesting, and have suddenly been remembered after lurking in the dodgy old memory for years. You might spot them as we meander our way over the next however many pages. In fact, there are at least five in this Introduction, and to start you off, one is obviously The Kinks, from 1968 "Days." You'll find one more Ray Davies quote later on, in chapter 27 by the way.

Oh, and you might wonder why I like using idiosyncratic or archaic words and phrases. Well, I just do. And I like using unnecessary Capital Letters at the start of some words, as did the Panaceans. Where I've quoted them, just assume I've put 'sic.'

I hope all this will make you smile a few times, and perhaps make you think differently about some things. Some parts might seem unconnected, but it will make sense if you read to the end. But most of all, I hope you enjoy it. Just use your imagination

The Boat – One Tuesday Afternoon 2015

During school holidays, grandparents are often given the contract to look after their grandchildren, and they look forward to it. They pretend they have other things to do that will now have to be put off, and keep quiet about how much these days cost. However, they are definitely not at all pleased if they aren't offered the chance to put back Time, grandfathers especially perhaps remembering guiltily how they wish they could have spent more time with their own children thirty years before. Children, like dogs, are a built-in excuse to do things you might not do if alone.

On a boat on a river, in a small town in the sun, Tula Sunshine and Poppy Star were having one of those afternoons in the school holiday that children remember years afterwards. Nothing spectacular happened – it was just that they enjoyed the new experience. The John Bunyan boat cruised the river Ouse in Bedford, taking sightseers on a leisurely floating tour of the Embankment and beyond.

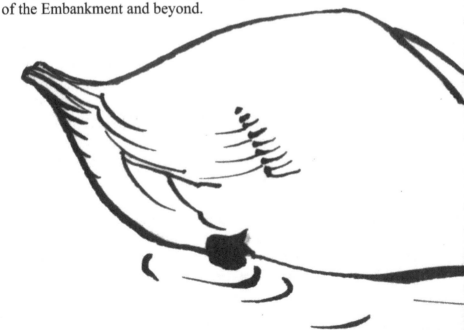

They had gone in one direction, cruising past gangs of swans that couldn't care less until they were put out by the boat's wake and looked offended. A couple of scullers went in the opposite direction, as if going to an urgent meeting. Poppy shouted at them to go faster, but Tula was worried that the swans might be hurt. The volunteer guide pointed out interesting buildings and told stories about the history of the river.

" Now we are going upstream, as far as the Sikh temple. You'll be able to see it shining in the sunlight. It's a magnificent building – not as spectacular as some, but wonderful all the same. It just goes to show how committed religious groups can be to their faith even when in a distant country. It's a shame that as you see it in the distance, you'll also see empty cans floating in the river beside you. That part of the river isn't so nice as the part we are in at the moment. Oh, I nearly forgot, if you look to the right, in that road, Newnham Road, there's a unique museum. Not many people have heard of it. It's the Panacea Museum, which tells the story of a strange religious group that was set up here in Bedford. It's a lovely peaceful place to go. I recommend it."

The grandmother looked at the girls, and smiled as they did what she thought they'd do – they were both sitting with fingers in their ears, and grinning at each other.

"Oh No" said Poppy "That's where grandad works. He keeps going on about it all the time. I don't want to hear it all again."

Tula quietly replied to nobody in particular " But it's cool though."

Their grandmother thought to herself that he did go on a bit about it. Perhaps he should write a book about it one day, get it out of his system. Yes, that would keep him out from under her feet for some time.

Forever Six O'clock- 1874

This was the best book Mabel had ever read. One of her very clever relations had given it to her and she couldn't stop talking about it to her grandmother's old maid, Murray. In the way that children of a certain age suddenly can't stop reading, learning new things, and asking endless questions, she was obsessed with the mystery and sheer magic of the tale. She was spontaneous and passionate, but stayed on the right side of the irritating precociousness that might earn her criticism. She liked the pictures and the riddles, but most of all she loved the strange and wonderful world that she could live in for hours and hours. Given to her on her eighth birthday, she would keep the book forever.

Murray adored her, her " little darling" and tried her best to make life as secure as she could after Mabel's father had died. She reassured her, praised her, told her she was special, let her have her way. "I'm the topmost brick on the chimney, aren't I, Murray!" Yes, she was.

But no-one,not even her clever relations, could explain some things in the book. Alice was her hero, but in the book she didn't like someone named Mabel. That Mabel lived in a poky little house, had no toys to play with, and had ever so many lessons to learn. Why couldn't Mr Carroll have called her something else? And why did the Dormouse always draw only things that began with the letter "M"? She thought she approved of "moon, memory and muchness" (whatever that was) but M was also for "mousetraps." And M was for March Hare, who was mad, and according to Murray, the Hatter was also mad. Murray always called him the Mad Hatter, even though Mabel didn't know why.

However many times she read the book, she could only ever read "Hatter" but never "Mad Hatter" although the Cheshire Cat also said he was mad, but what could a cat know? Perhaps some people seemed sensible but were mad really.

In unhappy times, Mabel often read " Alice's Adventures in Wonderland" and parts of it stayed in her mind, suddenly jumping out from the shadows in adulthood, taking her by surprise, and reminding her of the simple loving heart of her childhood. She, like Alice, would try to make sense of a strange world, she would gather about her other little children, she would feel all their sorrows and simple joys.

The telling of "Alice" was on a perfect happy summers day, in a perfect world. A strange world, but it was definitely a Paradise.

The Full Mabel-At the Museum
10.30 one Thursday in 2015
How it all Started

(Right then, I'd better have a practice talk to myself, ready for the group coming in later. Many visitors really enjoy the visit but don't hear about all the things that make the place so fascinating, so I'm going to give them "The Full Mabel"and then they can get a proper feel for what started here a hundred years ago).

"Good morning, and welcome to the museum. I understand that you don't know anything about the story of the Panacea Society, only that this is a fascinating place with a strange history. In fact, if you look at our Visitors' Book or Trip Advisor comments, the most used words are variations on "fascinating, weird, remarkable, strange and wonderful." So I think there's a good chance you'll enjoy your visit as well. There's a lot to see, and I think the best way to go about it is for me to tell you the whole story, but please join in with questions and comments as we go along from one place to another. People often have completely the wrong idea about the believers who lived here, so it's best to get the true story."

(There are normally two likely answers to my first question when visitors come in, as they stare at the Victorian flooring and the staircase in front of them. Often they come in very slowly, cautiously, perhaps expecting something to jump out at them, and after all it's the kind of place where you'd half expect to see a Victorian Missy standing still and quiet at the top of the stairs. It can be a bit novemberish. But there's no need to be wary, as we are all very nice normal people, not weirdos, and all the Society members are dead now. In fact the picture on the wall over there shows two of the last members, who also look perfectly normal. The lady is Ruth Klein who died in 2012, and

after that the Society itself ended. Some visitors remember seeing her feeding the swans on the river, as she lived only a stone's throw away. Looks very regal, I always think.

I ask people whether they've been here before, and if they have, they often say that they found it so interesting that they've come back again and brought a friend along as well.

If they haven't been here before, you often find that they have heard rumours or speculation about this place. One chap recently said "Never been here, but I know all about them. I've lived in Bedford all my 75 years, so I know. They were all a load of mad women, who had a box that must never be opened or else the world will end. They were all moneygrabbers and loonies. They had secrets."

Well, yes, I can understand how he thought that, but he was completely wrong. They were mostly harmless and although they were a strange lot, they were Bedford's strange lot. Something to shout about).

"The Panacea Society was a religious group, set up just after the Great War by a woman called Mabel Barltrop. As you'll find out, they had some beliefs that you might find strange but they are all dead now, so you can think or say whatever you like. We all do. I'm not of any formal religion myself, but if you are, and if I seem a bit dubious about it all as we go along, please don't be offended. I think they were a fascinating bunch - but just rather misguided. Yes, they were strange, but unlike many religious groups in history they did more Good than Harm. Probably the only harm they did was to themselves or each other, but as they were secretive, rumours grew up about them, and if something is secret people often think the worst.

Anyway, the first thing to know is that the Society was a Millenarian group. No, that doesn't mean they made hats (though looking at some old photos of their Garden Parties, some seemed to have been a very shrewd judge of a good hat) but that they believed in the Millennium. They expected the imminent return of Christ, who would bring 1000 years of Heaven on Earth. They would be the chosen ones to experience this Apocalypse, the Millennium, the Day of Revelation as set out in the Bible, a book they knew well from close study. There have been lots of groups like this - you know the kind, often in America, the ones who say that the world is going to end on, say, the 25th December 1953, and they go to live high on a mountain to wait for it to happen. Then when the 26th comes along and nothing has happened they say oh dear we've made a small mistake and in fact it will be 9 October 2018 ....and so it goes on and on, forever probably.

Our group, the Panaceans, thought that the world was going through such great changes that surely the Day of Revelation must be imminent. There were worrying upheavals in Society in the early Twentieth Century - The Great War, Communism, Socialism, and the disruption caused by disaffected groups such as the Unions and the Suffragettes. These must be the work of Satan.

They knew their Bible backwards, almost literally. At one time, for fun perhaps, they as a group read the Bible backwards. I don't know if this was each word or chapter, or just the New Testament before the Old, which I suppose is more likely."

(Two very different Gods, aren't they. The New Testament preaches compassion and forgiveness, turn the other cheek, love thy neighbour, whereas the God of the Old Testament is a cruel one who wants an eye for an eye and encourages smiting your enemies).

"They could find passages in the Old Testament prophets to show that the Millennium was imminent, so they had to prepare themselves for it. They did this by living in a community, admitting to and then trying to get rid of their faults by a process called Overcoming. They were trying to make themselves better and worthy of Heaven on Earth.

The leader, Mabel Barltrop, was the widow of a Church of England curate who had died shortly after they moved to Bedford, leaving her with four young children. After the war, she gathered a small group of similar minded people who she encouraged to move to Bedford, to form a community. They were almost all Anglicans and were mainly middle class Edwardian ladies with some money behind them, and all intensely religious. Over time there were some men who joined, often former soldiers who had perhaps been traumatised in the war. There were ex-suffragists, a Suffragette, and other women frustrated by the lack of opportunity to use their talents in early twentieth century England. Working class people were allowed, but only as servants; after all, even in God's kingdom, some people must be more equal than others. They bought houses, known as Community Houses, in this part of town – the nicest part of town – and prepared for Salvation.

This building we are in, number 9 Newnham Road, was a Community property but a very special one. I'll tell you more in a bit, after you've looked around these rooms, and some more about their beliefs."

(I normally let the visitors look around at this point, and they have already come to some conclusions about what they have learnt so far. It's a mixture of fascination, disbelief and respect. The respect is for the fact that this was largely a female community, run and led by women, with former suffragists playing an important part. Some visitors link this to the ideals of the Hippie communes of the 1960's or the Women's Lib movement, and perhaps there are some similarities. There is also respect from the most religious visitors, who might imagine that if born a hundred years before, they too might have devoted their lives to preparation for immortality, as the Panaceans did.

There's much, much more for them to see and hear, but at the moment they are trying to imagine what the people who came here must have been like, to imagine the people who imagined that Eden was here. Oh yes, I'll tell them next that they will be going into the Garden of Eden, as the Panaceans believed Bedford was the site of the original Eden.

Sometimes I also wonder what they were like, and of course they were all different people - they surely can't have been identikit robots. In the archives, their diaries and so on don't tell everything about their character, so almost anything you imagine is feasible and valid, as long as based on study of the evidence.

So let's imagine the story of someone who came here. Let's imagine someone who might have imagined Eden. Let's give her an interesting name. Let's imagine a story. Let's call her Etholle).

Etholle
In The Beginning

Well, here's my story, the story of a girl called Etholle.

Mrs Gwynne had often said I should keep a diary so I could remember all the things that happened to me, and I started just after I came to live with her in Bedford. I didn't do anything with the diaries until a while ago my good neighbour Meg read some of them and said I ought to put them into an autobiography, the story of what I had done and seen. I thought nothing much had happened in my life, till she told me I had lived in Interesting Times and met interesting people, so that's what I've done.

I began the diaries in 1922, when I was 19. The things that happened before that I couldn't remember exactly, but Meg reckoned I should write it anyway so I have included lots of memories as I remember them. They might not be completely accurate but by and large they are right. After 1922, everything is as I put in my diaries.

When I've been writing I sometimes get carried away and go from one thing to another, but it does make sense to me. All those strange things did happen, even the vicar who was eaten by a lion. As I get older, my memory is starting to pack up, so I'll probably finish when I start to go ga-ga rather than write things that might not be true.

I started writing this story in 1969, as Meg said I should get going on it before it was too late. I've written the bits up to 1969 as if I wrote them at the time as Meg thought it would look better that way and seem more realistic. Mrs G often told me to use proper words, not the dialect I was brought up to use ("why should I try to talk correct?" I thought at the time). As a result, I've tried to do that, but things do slip out from time to time.

Now I've got up to 1985 and I think I'll have to stop soon, as I can't see very well and my handwriting is getting shaky. I keep going forwards and backwards as I remember things. They are all important so I have to jot them down, but I do sometimes lose sense of Time. Actually, I think Meg was right. I really have seen some interesting things, and strange people. I shew my writings to Meg and she can have them one day. The Clancys have been like a family to me as I don't have a real family myself. What she'll do with it all I don't know. It might be worth reading.

So here's what I remember....but some things are better left unsaid.

I sometimes wondered whether there was something wrong with my memory; it seemed to be different from those of other people. In the few biographies or autobiographies I've read, there were loads of details and stories about someone's early life, almost from birth, and written so convincingly that they must be true. People could apparently remember, word for word, conversations they had had years before. I can't do that. They could also point out important events that had shaped their character and life, putting them on a particular road to adulthood, career or destiny. However much I've tried, I can only remember a few things about my childhood before I came to the Community. But some of these things are in a lot of detail and looking back, might have helped shape my life.

I can't remember my mother, but think she must have died when I was young. A thin man with a moustache appeared occasionally, and was very nice to me and I think he must have been my father, but nobody told me so. He told me the difference between rooks and crows. I can still remember his smell. He smelt clean. I was brought up by a series of elderly ladies who fed me, told me what to do, taught me the "paths of righteousness" and then passed me over to another elderly lady. All of them made sure I went to church and knew my way around the Bible. They all had a faintly musty smell, which I thought was because of their religious way of life.

The clear memories I do have are of the seaside. I remember being a small child, wandering about looking at interesting things in the sand, playing, and then meandering around again. Somehow (as children are often able to do) I must have invited myself into a group of people. A right little mawther I must have been.The sand was hot and I wanted to dance. For some reason I told them my name was Felicity. Presumably they were kind people, as they looked after me till the man with the moustache found me, glad that I was found rather than angry that I had strayed away. I remember he held me tight for a long while. "Do you never do that agin my gal" he said. A lot of parents would have got a right cob on, but he didn't. The people made me feel safe and glad to be in their group. The ladies were sensibly dressed, with smart sun-hats, and the men wore ties and straw-boaters. There were lots of older children, who had played with me and made me laugh. I remember being happy there. A few years later I found a newspaper cutting, a photograph taken in 1908 of what must have been that event. It was a meeting of religious groups on the sands at Sheringham. In the photo were what I'm sure must have been the kind people I had felt at home with – one of the children looked like me, so it must be true. They had banners, naming the people as members of the Children's Special Service Mission. One banner read "By Grace are Ye Saved through Faith" and "CSSM Ventnor." Other places were named on banners – Deal, Hunstanton, Croydon, and France. Another read "CSSM Africa for Christ." Just looking at the photo made me feel happy. I used to look at the picture and sing one of my favourite hymns, loudly and without a care in the world. I've still got the picture.

Then there is the memory of "The Garden of Sleep," a peaceful place where one of my guardians sometimes took me. I remember it took a long time to get there by the cart, and try as I might to stop myself I normally drowsed on both journeys. I definitely remember sitting on the cliff looking out to sea, with the stone tower high above me. There were graves marked and the gulls landed close by, hoping for scraps from my food. Sometimes I'd go chasing rabbits.There were endless fields of poppies inland and I decided red was the best colour in the world - especially as my own hair was an auburn colour. Still is, but a bit faded. If alone there I liked to dance about, singing. Sometimes other people were there having a picnic, and I was told that I used to gain confidence and would often go and ask the groups if they agreed with me that this must be the most wonderful place in the world. They would all say that surely I was right – there was no better place to be.

Once, there was a long-haired gipsy girl there, playing the fiddle ever so fast and she could play faster than I could dance and it was better than listening to the skylarks. Her name was Hulda. I thought that was a funny old name to wake up with every morning, but I liked it.

Near the end of the Great War, when I was 15, I went there again, by myself. I took a sixpence, my shut-knife and a piece of string, as someone once told my that was all you ever needed to carry with you for a journey to anywhere. I rode my bike, so I was awake all the way unlike before. It rained. No people there. The tower had gone, fallen over the cliff like the rest of the church building. There were no poppies in the September fields, and not even any gnats or dandelion clocks to blow. And no birds sang.The place was no longer magical. I had never felt so sad in my life, as my little piece of heaven once so real, had gone. "Too much of a Good Thing. Always partridge" my guardian told me. "We cannot be truly happy on this earth."

I must have been different from the other girls in the several villages where I stayed. I was slower at picking things up in school, and soon that frustrated the teachers, except for old Miss Mort. Most of the other pupils thought I was the dunce, but I was always the first to help others when I could and in my way I think I was well-liked but never realised it at the time. I was the best in class at Country Dancing, with my long auburn hair the centre of the action and with an enormous smile on my face as I rollicked about. "Pre - Raphaelite" one teacher said. "But those stunners were not too bright and no better than they should be. She'd be better off listening more in class." I didn't know what that meant. But the thing about listening was the problem – I couldn't hear as well as others, and although I did try, I was never going to keep up. I also had a slight stutter, that showed itself if I was thinking before I opened my mouth, but if I just sort of let myself go and spoke without thinking beforehand, it disappeared. The ideas came to me well enough, but my speech wasn't clear, so it was easy to decide I couldn't think or write properly. I became a Jonah.

I remember a lovely poem I wrote when the teacher told us to write about Spring:

" Spring, Spring, Spring is here
And all the little baby things are born."

I thought it was good, but some of the class laughed because I shouted it out so loudly that the class next door could hear. They called me "Luggy" Andrews.

I think people looked on me as a bit simple but with a kind heart. At one point I was put into the Kelling Children's Sanatorium, after my face developed a deformity on one side. The nurses there were good to me, though I heard about other girls who were very unhappy there. One girl said she was very special, as her name was Perseid. Another was funny, always calling the doctors "Baldy." My illness might be something called Bell's Palsy or Lockjaw, they thought, and eventually it virtually disappeared but for some time I looked different. Even in adult life my face occasionally looks a little sinister when I talk. So the answer was simple – don't talk unless absolutely necessary, and I might be able to just slip into the background. Even without the slightly uneven mouth that the illness gave me I wasn't sure if I was reasonably inoffensive in looks or downright ugly, not realising that apparently there are some women that can be both at the same time. Meg says that the French call that "jolie-laide"- being pretty and ugly at the same time. She says some men find that very attractive in a woman, but that women normally don't realise it. So, perhaps a few men might even have have found me attractive in the past, now I think about it, But I'm old now, and I've missed the boat.

I'll die wondering.

The end result was that at 15, I must have been very insecure and lacking in confidence. No mother. No proper father. Brought up by apparently accidental guardians. Considered backward. Frustrated. Ugly. But I had had glimpses of being comfortable, in the religious group, at the Garden of Sleep, and in the occasional carefree times when I could just let myself go.

When they told me that the man with the moustache was dead, I think I took it all in easily. After all, I hardly saw him, and he was no more important to me than that shabby-clothed man at the shop who might give me a few extra sweets for some reason. People said he had coarse thoughts. One guardian told me my father was a hero like all the others who had died in the war, so I asked people who was the biggest hero they knew about. No-one said my father. Some said Horatio Nelson, and some said the local hero was Henry Blogg, the bravest man in England. Like many others, my father had no funeral as there was no body found.

So many were lost at sea that day. So many.

I remember making a lovely snowman once, but cried when it melted.

One night, I woke up and saw wonderful blue green and red lights waving and beckoning to me from out at sea. It was so pretty that it felt like I was halfway to Heaven. Inland, a dog fox was barking, so it sounded magical as well. Everyone else said I had just imagined it all. The next morning, when my latest guardian asked if I would like to go somewhere that I could sing hymns and be in a group of people like I had met on the beach, and be in the most wonderful place on earth, I smiled and nodded my head straight away. The lights must have been a sign that I should go. It would be not just a peaceful place, but Heaven on Earth, they said. I hoped it wouldn't be too serious a place as my "home" life wasn't much fun. Everything revolved around the Church, and although I never told them, when I was younger I'd thought that God was some kind of a machine. I imagined that we had to go to church lots of times every week in order to keep God going: we had to wind him up, like clockwork. But now things were changing. The guardian said she'd make the arrangements, and before too long, I was on the way to a new life.

The Full Mabel
A Very English Messiah

(Time to get going again. With any group you get some who want to stay in every room for ages, and others who want to hurry to the next one as quickly as possible to see what's coming next. They might miss out on the most interesting things, so I encourage them to come back another day, with a friend of course, to find things they might have missed the first time around).

Let's carry on with a bit more about Mabel Barltrop and her followers.

Ever since Mabel's early life in Croydon, she had been used to rubbing shoulders with some very bright people. She was from a conventional Victorian middle class family, well enough off to have a servant, but not more than that. She was born Mabel Andrews in 1866, and had an unlucky time of it as her father died when she was young, her mother was permanently ill, and her older brother also died when he was young. Her aunt Fanny was a great help to the family financially, and she took Mabel under her wing to help in her education and social development.

Mabel was gently introduced to the world of well-educated people, clever people who she admired and respected. One cousin, Eliza Orme, was the first female barrister in England, and Mabel had a small scale correspondence with the great Victorian John Ruskin.

She thought a great deal about theological matters, and it was perhaps no surprise when she married a lowly Anglican curate, Arthur Barltrop. He hadn't gone to the right school or university, so he never progressed – promotion depended a lot on background. They moved to Bedford, partly because Arthur's sister Lennie lived there, married to a Thomas Bull – yes, that's the Bull family that still has the jewellery shop in Bedford. They lived at 12 Albany Road, just a few yards from here, in a modest end-terrace house. They had four children, Eric, Ivan, Adrian and Dilys. Sadly, Arthur died not long after they moved, and Mabel suffered from depression. Fanny moved in with them and again helped financially. Mabel made a small income from reviewing theological and other religious books and magazines, and although she became a very respected authority in this area, she did so under the pseudonym Mark Proctor. After all, in those days a woman couldn't be expected to have a brain big enough to even think about complicated matters, let alone write about them.

Through this connection with theological writing, she gradually started correspondence with other women across the country, women who had similar interests, but were frustrated by the Church of England's refusal to take women seriously. The Church of England might well request a woman's presence at the Vicarage for tea and a cucumber sandwich, but little else. The excellent postal service in those days made quick correspondence possible. The women were mostly Anglicans, often with a close family member being a clergyman. Perhaps the most important were Kate Firth, Rachel Fox and Ellen Oliver.

Kate Firth was a good friend of hers, and bought a large house called The Haven, next door to where we are now. Eventually they fell out when Kate decided Mabel's beliefs were nonsensical and she moved away, but early on it was quite possible that Kate might have become the leader of the group. Rachel Fox was a Quaker, from the Fox family that was so important in the founding of the Quakers. She lived in Cornwall, but stayed in Bedford as much as possible and eventually moved here. She wrote several books on the story of the Society, and was the unofficial historian of the group. Ellen Oliver was a former Suffragette who had once been in Holloway prison for her activism, a very intense woman who had firm belief in any crusade she supported.

Whereas Ellen Oliver was involved in the quite extreme Women's Social and Political Union, and the less extreme but definitely feminist White Cross League (to do with matters of Women and S*x), Alice Jones was in the more conservative Church League for Women's Suffrage, and another founder, Gertrude Searson, was also a suffragist but firmly against violent action. In 1919 Mabel was 53 years old, and her followers were also in their 50's or 60's. None were "war widows," but more typically were spinsters, or conventional widows, often with all the frustrations of looking after a close relation, but with little freedom for themselves. Most were used to a life where they had at least one servant to look after them.

It wasn't until 1920 that the first significant male member joined, Peter Rasmussen.

Mabel's first son, Eric, was killed in the war and it was partly this that led to a further period of depression in her life in 1915. After the war ended, the group became stronger and more intense, with women moving to Bedford to be nearer the centre of activity. Being rich, they tended to buy houses in this part of town near the Embankment, as it was the most refined.

(Of course, I've left out the fact that during both periods of depression she was put into mental institutions, but I'll come on to that later. The second time it was way more than depression – probably delusional, as she heard voices. And the second time was triggered not by her son's death but by the refusal of the Church of England to agree to ...but I'll come to that later as well. Mabel's first son Eric was never a member, nor was the second, Ivan,who emigrated to Canada. Adrian was, on and off, but only her daughter Dilys was a committed member, though eventually she disowned them).

The main thing that linked these Middle Class ladies was their expectation of the coming millennium, and in particular their interest in the writings of someone called Joanna Southcott. Southcott claimed to be a great prophet, and had died a hundred years before. She was the most important of a series of modern English prophets known as The Visitation. In their different ways they foretold that before Jesus could return for the Millennium, there would have to be another prophet called Shiloh, who would prepare the way, just as John the Baptist had done for him the first time. Southcott claimed to be pregnant and would give birth to the baby Shiloh (a dodgy sort of claim to make, as she was 64 years old and still a virgin). Anyway, she died in 1814 without having a baby. She also claimed to hear messages that prophesied the future, and she wrote them down and kept them in a sealed box.

In the early part of the twentieth century there was a renewed interest in Joanna Southcott, mainly due to the writings of Helen Shepstone and Alice Seymour, and it was because of this that Mabel's group grew. Mabel gradually became the leader of the group, and in February 1919 Ellen Oliver came to the conclusion that Mabel was in fact Shiloh, the spiritual incarnation of the baby that Southcott hadn't had. She wrote to Kate Firth in excited fashion declaring this great revelation, and from that point on, the group went viral, as you might say nowadays.

(I love to see how quickly some visitors really get into the whole Mabel experience. One lady asked if she could bring her small dog in and of course I said yes as we are sensible here, and after seeing the introductory video she renamed the dog Shiloh. You can't help smiling, can you. Most are impressed by the elaborate crib made ready for Southcott's baby Shiloh, though one visitor thought it looked like something out of 'Rosemary's Baby').

OK. Time for another small break while you look around this room, and then I'll tell you more about how Mabel became famous internationally.

(That letter Ellen Oliver wrote with the revelation about Mabel

being Shiloh must surely be one of the most important things in the history of the Society or even of the world as far as they were concerned. But at the end of it, after the dramatic revelation, she says something like "I am so sorry about your burst pipe and that you have a cold." Blimey, talk about going from the Sublime to the Ridiculous. But that's what they were like – full of strange contradictions and illogicalities. In her diary, Ellen Oliver once wrote that she woke up to a wonderful sunny Spring morning ....and then spent the whole day tidying her room. One day all she did was write a letter, and the next day all she did was post it. They had a nice easy life in the main, and their ideas of Equality for Women perhaps didn't go much further than looking after their own class.

I wonder how Etholle is getting on ...).

Etholle
Coming To Bedford

(I forgot to say, although I was certainly no scholar when I was at school I was naturally clever, or so people said. After I came to Bedford Mrs Gwynne realised this, and did all she could to teach me the things I'd missed out on. I was good at English, especially writing stories that I could make up, and I loved hearing about lands far away where the sun shone all day long. I'd make up plays and concerts for her, and she'd be as pleased as punch at the things I'd come out with. No one else knew that she was the person who gave me my education).

The church ladies packed me up with all I would need – some clothes and an old Bible. Before I went four of the church ladies who had looked after me sat me down in a fusty front room, gave me a cup of weak tea, and explained my past and what was to happen next. My mother, the daughter of a curate, had been sinful. She had disgraced herself and her family, and I had been the result. My grandparents had made arrangements for God-fearing families in the area to bring me up in the right way, but not to tell me about my past until I was more knowing. The grandparents themselves had moved away for good. My mother had died in childbirth. No-one acknowledged the thin man with a moustache as my father but I'm sure he was. They admitted that some guardians turned a blind eye when he tried to have some kind of contact with me, but others built barriers so he could only see me from time to time. He had asked that they would give me his one piece of advice: Be Kind. They passed on this advice, and so now their duties were all ended.

They shew me my mother's Bible, but it didn't have details of family dates or names in it as I'd hoped. The front pages were ...blank. Yes, it was a family Bible, but there were no details of my family; all I had there was the word of my grandfather's God. Later, when I was in Bedford, someone sent me a photograph of my father and I have it still, hidden in a secret place.

The guardians had the job of mapping my future, and it had been decided that I would live with the widow of a vicar in Bedford. I was from the right religious background, so I should fit in there but at the same time my lack of parents meant I could be considered an embarrassment in normal society. They had made enquiries and it seemed that the widow thought I might have a future there. The lady I was going to live with was on good terms with another widow of a vicar, but who had had unlucky setbacks in her own life, and who might now help me to a better life.

The explanations about my past seemed to make sense, but it was all unfair. I hadn't done anything wrong, I hadn't sinned, I was surely guiltless. Men and women of the Church should show compassion and not disown me. The Sermon on the Mount would hint that Jesus would sympathise with me, not ignore me. These women were false in their attitudes – I had heard them talk nastily about a local cleric at Stiffkey, who had forgiven his wife for some bad liaison with another man, and taken the resultant child as his own. This man, Harold Davidson, was also criticised for his work in helping what they called Fallen Women in London. It was all confusing, Christians acting in ways that didn't seem Christian to me. But I had to put up with it and now I was going to this new place. Of course, I was too scared to say any of that.

None of my guardians had been horrible to me, but I think they must have been very strict. It was all "Speak when you're spoken to" or "Do as you're told" or "Be seen but not heard" but as I hadn't known any other way of life I just thought it was normal, and never moaned about it. It was like being at school all the time. In fact this turned out to be good in a way, as later on I found that Panacea Society life was very similar, so I was used to it.

I can't remember the names of any of my guardians. I can't remember anyone giving me a cuddle. I never had a proper friend. When I left it was a quick tear-free goodbye. It only took a moment.

Kind strangers must have taken pity on me, the unworldly young girl who somehow managed the longest journey of her life so far in May 1919. My guardians had told me that God would guide me to the address in Bedford, and no doubt he had arranged the train timetables so that this was easy. Some railway staff had pointed out to me, the red haired girl, which were the right trains to get on, and I arrived at Bedford. At the station there was no-one to meet me and everyone was rushing about as if on a mission. I didn't dare ask anyone, so I meandered about for a few minutes hoping to see a road sign that said Castle Road, though for some reason I kept thinking it was Canticle Street.

Just when I was at the point of tears, and sat down at the roadside on the small suitcase carrying my world, an angel came to help me. "Where to, ma'am?" said a voice. The bus driver looked at me with a broad smile. "You lost?" I must have stuttered that I was going to see Mrs Gwynne at an address in Castle Road, and the man paused slightly, then in a loud happy voice, said "Well that's where I'm going. Come on in ma'am." He must have seen the tears of relief and joy behind the long hair, and thought better of asking for the fare. I sat down near the front of the almost empty bus and politely waited as it went round unknown roads. Outside, people were walking quickly, with a purpose, presumably going home as it was early evening. I remember everyone seemed to know where they were going. I stared at the driver, who from time to time shouted out the names of roads, looked in his mirror, and always said something nice to passengers who got off. He was black. I had never seen a black man before in my old world, and couldn't remember ever having heard people talk about them. He was different – smiling, cheerful, kind and optimistic – and those were words I could not have used to describe the people in the world I'd just left.

I didn't know at the time that Joe altered his route to make sure he could stop along the Embankment, and then direct me the short distance to the part of Castle Road that I wanted. I didn't know that other passengers had been quietly huffing and puffing about the driver being on the drag, not knowing the right route, delaying them. But I did know that I was grateful for his Samaritan act. He was a good man. I thanked him, and walked the short distance to my new home, put down my case, stood tall, brushed my coat, and knocked on the door. Just as the door opened, I thought of Joe's smile, and the Kindness of Strangers.

(Later, I heard that Joe had come to England years before, and had been an ambulance driver in the War. Perhaps he too had needed help when he came from Jamaica and remembered how it felt, so he helped me in the way that someone had helped him - or perhaps in the way he wished to have been helped, but that no one had offered him. So he was kind and brave, like my father may have been. In the years that followed, I often saw him driving his bus and if he saw me he would wave. I couldn't hide my red hair! I was pleased a few years later when he became higher up in the world, by driving his own taxi. In November he sometimes decorated his bus with wreaths and poppies, and had signs saying Loos, Marne and Mons, and raised money for the Poppy Fund).

The Full Mabel
Strange People - Strange Ideas

—————⊳◆⊲—————

(We get a very interesting cross-section of people visiting. By now, you know which ones are REALLY interested and wanting more and more, or the ones who have an attractive personality, or the inquisitive ones. As the headline used to say: "All Human Life is Here." I don't think I've yet come across a visitor who has been rude or objectionable. They are a good lot. Sally, that's you by the way.

They are interested in different aspects of what they see and hear. Quite a few are interested in the idea of the Millennium, and Apocalyptic groups generally. For these, I mention the high level research sponsored by the Panacea Trust into such groups. If you are interested, and I suspect you are, these groups generally have five common characteristics:

The Salvation/Apocalypse will be collective. It happens to a group, not to individuals.

It is imminent. It will be soon, and sudden.

It will be total. It will completely change life on Earth.

It will be terrestrial. Salvation will be on Earth, not in Heaven.

There will be some kind of supernatural agency involved to bring it about.

In Christian belief, the thousand years of Heaven on Earth will begin or end with the second Coming of Christ.

Ok, that's enough of that. This isn't a lecture. Let's carry on with the tour. The visitors are waiting...).

After Ellen Oliver outed Mabel as Shiloh, the group became more and more convinced that their leader was someone really special. Rachel Fox said she should be called Octavia as she was the eighth prophet of the Visitation, following Helen Shepstone, who they renamed Helen Exeter. Mabel was always grateful for Helen Shepstone's activities in promoting the work of Joanna Southcott, and right up till her death Mabel had a picture of Shepstone in her bedroom. Mabel did nothing to discourage followers from giving her this new status as a prophet and they gave her gifts, presumably to be in the Inner Circle of the leader.

Things started to get more and more unbelievable. Mabel heard voices, had messages from God at 5.30 every day and wrote them down by automatic writing. They were known as the Daily Scripts. She started taking services for her small group in the Upper Room of her house. She appointed Apostles. She declared that Bedford was the site of the original Garden of Eden, and the centre was, of course, her house. She must not walk more than 77 steps from her house, or else Satan would get her. She was the Daughter of God. She had miraculous powers of healing. She was the one who would drive Satan from the world.

She came to the conclusion that her late husband Arthur was a reincarnation of Jesus. All these strange developments were accepted by her followers. A few did fall by the wayside, but if the others had any doubts they said nothing.

(Helen Shepstone seems to have been a fairly sensible person compared with Mabel, although she was prone to wearing silly hats. The appointment of Apostles could be seen as a blasphemous act, but if Mabel was God's daughter then surely she could do the same as her brother Jesus. What we would see as a paradox, though, is that the apostles were chosen so as to have different astrological star signs – we don't associate sincere religious beliefs with Astrology. In a short autobiography, Mabel gave only a few details of her husband, but did mention that he was good at growing lettuces, and that he once took five wickets in six balls playing cricket. His status as the second incarnation of Jesus was not declared to all followers, but her inner circle were told and as none said this was blasphemous, it came to be taken as true by the most important members).

Others in the group were also convinced that they heard voices though not, like Mabel, from God. They saw hidden messages in the shape of bushes in the Garden. They found complicated ways to link world events to obscure verses in the Old Testament. If they heard a knock on the door, but no one was there, they were sure it must have been Jesus, and would then carry on as normal. Mabel's first secretary, Jessie Johnson, had an amazing ability to "speak with tongues" and had definite plans for the future of the group, but was edged out for being too forward, and for having ideas with which Mabel disagreed. It was Jessie Johnson who first put forward the idea that "Bedford is the place of God's glory" and perhaps it was this that helped encourage followers to move to Bedford.

Oh yes, I said I'd come on to the international fame that the Society achieved, so we'll look at that next – it's worth waiting for ....

(A few thoughts on common misconceptions and quirks to do with things biblical. Can I let off steam?

A while ago, a visitor got very excited when I told her she would be going into the Garden of Eden. "Is there an apple tree?" she asked.

"Oh yes, definitely" I said.

"Can I have an apple please?"

"Yep."

What a confident chap I was. She was the kind of person who you could chat with all day long.

"Is there a snake?"

That shut me up; there was no snake.

Damn, I thought. I don't like visitors to be disappointed. The next day I put things right - I helped myself to my dog's play snake and put it in the garden. An excellent idea, and not a Marketing type in sight. Nobody has had a heart attack because of it yet. And no-one will ever steal it, because surely all our visitors are nice.

The snake in the garden is called Edgar – Mabel would have approved. You'll find out why later.

*Anyway, the point is that the Bible doesn't mention an **apple**, but **fruit,** the fruit of knowledge. So how could anyone paint or draw Eden if this important bit isn't clear? Ancient scholars argued that it could be a grape or a fig or a tamarind or an olive. Eventually Christians in the Northern Europe pressure group won the argument – it must be* *an apple, because the Latin word for apple, malum, also means Evil. Conveniently, apples grew well in northern Europe whereas grapes and figs were too exotic to live there. The clincher was that the apple had long been a pagan symbol of Knowledge.*

Nearly all visitors think that it is important to have an apple tree in the Garden of Eden, but they don't realise that its only because the Romans didn't have enough words in their vocabulary.

There's a similar problem that would have taxed the Panaceans' brains, involving two Greek words with just one letter difference: homoousian and homoousion.

Some early Christians believed that God was the only god, that Christ was the son of God, and that God's presence on the earth was via the Holy Spirit which produced the works of the prophets and the virgin birth. Together, they were the Holy Trinity. Others argued that if Christ was God's son then surely he must be inferior to God, and that the Holy Spirit must then be inferior to Christ.

The first group defined Christ in Greek as homoousian, meaning "of the same essence" as God i.e. the same thing, whereas the second group preferred homoousion, meaning "similar in essence" as God i.e. not the same thing as God and therefore inferior.

In the end, at the council of Nicaea in AD 325, it was decided that the first option would be enforced from then on, and so the concept of the Holy Trinity was established.

I wonder what the ancient theologians would have thought about the claims of a woman called Mabel 1600 years later, that she was God's daughter, and that God was made up of four bits, not three, but more of that later.

And another thing while I'm at it. All Religions seem to change into something not necessarily intended originally. In pagan times, humans imagined gods of the forest, the river, the air, and so on, and as a result they imagined holy trees, holy stones and holy rivers. In Christianity, there is only one God, but humans can't help but fiddle about with this idea, so that "Saints" materialised. In due course, there were saints with special responsibility for things like Travel (Christopher) the

Weather (Swithin) or Animals (Francis of Assisi). These saints became Small Gods (just like the gods of the forest or the river) and they had special powers to protect the people who have adopted them. It all gets a bit silly when countries, professions and disorders have patron saints: St Dennis (Headaches), St Bonaventura (Bowel disorders) or St Anthony (a busy chap, responsible for Lost articles, the poor, amputees and Cemetery workers). You can understand Luther's stand on this kind of thing.

All the dressing up, chants and smells are very impressive things, but are they much different from the pagan ceremony shown in 'The Wicker Man' albeit less violent? Does God really need all that stuff? And religious reasons have been the excuse for wars, persecution and killing throughout History. Surely any decent God would disapprove, yet followers of all religions fall back on their beliefs to justify their sometimes evil actions.

The Panaceans did no harm to other people; they were fanatics, but peaceful fanatics. Mostly harmless.

OK. Rant over, but as you chat to visitors, I'm sure that variations on the above thoughts are going through their minds, so let's get them out of the way).

Etholle
Singing For Zion

Although the town was bigger than the places I'd been used to, it suited me well. It was just big enough that it had all the things people could reasonably want – shops, cinemas and so on – but still small enough that you could easily walk from wherever you lived to the countryside. The river was only a few hundred yards away, where gentlemen with their fine ladies would stroll along the Embankment most days. I liked to see the swans, paddling along unconcerned with anything other than their own plans for the day, unless disturbed by the pleasure boats that made money for their owners in the summer. I loved the boats' names: Lorna Doone, and the Lodore. The River Festival was a big event that brought important people to the town, or so they said, but I never saw anyone mentioned in the newspapers, unless the short Welsh-sounding man with a twinkle in his eye was one. He had smiled at me as he came out of the Swan Hotel, and winked at me as well. He looked very distinguished, so perhaps he was someone who was someone.

My part of the town was ….genteel. The roads nearby had more than their fair share of what I thought were mansions, really just large houses overlooking the river. Apparently only twenty years before it was a slum area called Waterloo, but now it was very posh. As I traipsed about from one errand to another I soon recognised which servant worked at which house, and which child being pushed in which pram by which nanny belonged to which property. Occasionally there were less well-dressed people who came to the riverside, but there was normally a policeman not far away, to guard the town's guardians of decency. And their property. Just in case. And I got to know some of the wounded soldiers, still in ragged uniforms, who spent their time there. Harry had one leg, a set of medals, and a wife who disowned him. He stumbled from one seat to another every hour or so, to beg from passers-by. Some policemen, like Mr Chambers, turned a blind eye. Mr Chambers told me that he had single-handedly sorted out a riot at a Britannia Road pub called The Crown in 1915, but I think he exaggerated. Another old soldier, Albert, seemed normal but most days he would suddenly shout and scream and shake for no reason, and even when he calmed down, making his deep-sea diver sounds, he had the look of someone being chased by the Devil. I got used to him but at first he really gave me the willies. He never did anyone any harm. He slowly got thinner and more haggard, and at some point in 1919, he stopped coming to his usual places. Speculation was that he had fallen into the river, accidentally or otherwise, and drifted downstream. In any event the local householders did nothing to find out more, now less embarrassed about taking their comforts, and pleased that the air they breathed was fresher.

I always said Good Morning to anyone I met. Sometimes I even managed to get a reply from the occasional angler or two, as they usually pretended that their bit of the river needed their complete concentration. On the other hand, people walking dogs nearly always chatted with me. I wonder if there are any people who have a dog and also like fishing.

This part of town was quiet and peaceful, both discrete and discreet. The shopkeepers knew their customers and to some extent judged them by the servants they hired. Servants who aped the aloofness of puffed-up masters were treated less well than more down to earth types, and some acted like half-sixers themselves though they were only servants. I had always been able to get on with most kinds of people, so although they considered me as a lady, they also felt I was "one of them." Funny really, as I had always thought of myself as being below the salt anyway. Things had been different even just ten years before, but some could only carry on living with the old assumptions. I think they found me honest, open, and straight as a die. I gave compliments where they were due and never complained about anything. In reality although Mrs G played the aloof privileged lady in public, when inside the house we got on more like a wise grandmother quietly educating a youngster in the wisdoms that she wished she'd known when she herself was young. I worked that out quite quickly.

(Mrs G often told me not to get carried away with flowery language when I wrote things down. She said it's not right to use words you wouldn't use if talking to a friend. You should make it like a normal conversation. I do try, but sometimes I get carried away still. Writing discrete *and* discreet *was just trying to be clever, wasn't it. Amateurish. But let's keep it in anyway. I'm getting used to this now. It's fun).*

Later, Mrs G told me a bit about her story and what she'd thought of me when I came to her home.

Life had turned bad on Mrs G. Her husband had been a clergyman, and had been a chaplain to the forces in the war, but having survived, he had died in the influenza epidemic that followed. A good but apparently unremarkable woman, she missed the way he liked her funny little ways as much as anything else, and now depended more on a small circle of old friends in the area for companionship. She was an intelligent woman in her 60s, open to new ideas, but without him she had been unsure of herself. On that day, when her servant brought me into her room, she was struck by my innocence and openness, which for the first time for years made her feel maternal! They had never had children, though she had wanted them, and long ago had often cried with real tears when seeing ill treatment of children by their parents. As soon as I replied to questions, with my nervous stuttering voice, and in a different accent, Mrs G decided that her job was to look after me, even though I was up till then just a name to her. Her late husband had had friends or relations in Norfolk and one had offered me as a companion to educate. I don't think Mrs G knew much about the reasoning for all this, as her husband had always clammed up if asked about his time there.

She said I stuttered because someone must have tickled my feet too much when I was a baby, and I believed her. It was a little while before I realised that Mrs G often said things that were silly just to get a reaction or to see if people laughed. She was clever like that, because most people thought she was serious all the time. She also told me that I scrubbed up well, which I thought was a fine compliment. When I was younger, one of my guardians had told me to be quiet, as if I kept talking I'd use up all the words given to me by God for the day. People were only allowed a certain number. Mrs G told me that was just a way to make me shut up, but I'd always believed it was the truth, and so perhaps that was another reason I always kept myself to myself and didn't say much.

Mrs G gave me instructions on what I was to do, how I should do it, and the way I should behave. Her old servant was to stay for another month, but then I would be responsible for the running of the household until a new servant was hired. I was to be there every day apart from Tuesday and Thursday afternoons when I could do as I wanted, but must be back by 5.00. On those days Mrs G visited friends nearby.

That was all a load of twaddle really, as I ended up being responsible for the cooking and the cleaning and the mending and the shopping and generally making sure Mrs G had little to do, as the new servant never materialised. I enjoyed it all even though I'm not really a Little Sally Homemaker. I liked to be useful. And not all ladies of this class had a servant anyway, she said. I could have visitors, if approved of by Mrs G. She told me all this in a loud firm voice, sounding more authoritative than she really felt, but I was happy about this firmness. I had heard clearly what my place was, and could understand. So that's what I would do. In our different ways I think we both immediately respected each other. It would be rather embarrassing for someone like Mrs G not to be able to afford a servant, so in the eyes of some people I filled that role, but at the same time, I was a companion and a lady! I wasn't too forward with her though, at least not at first.

I remember that once, late at night, I saw her sitting alone in the dark, head in her hands, sobbing dolefully to herself **"She's lost control again. She's lost control."** I didn't like to ask questions but later on I found out what she meant. It made me uneasy, though later on things done by Mrs Goodwin really gave me the willies far more.

My room was cold, as was much of the house, and not as clean as

I was used to so on my first morning I set to scrubbing clean the stone floors. Mrs G had gone out, but as she opened the door she heard singing – something missing from the house for a long time. Loud, happy, joyful singing. She looked down the hallway, into the kitchen, and heard me singing as I scrubbed the floor:

"Daily, daily, sing the praises,
Of the city God hath made;
In the beauteous fields of Eden
Its foundation stones are laid.

O that I had wings of angels,
Here to spread and heavenward fly!
I would seek the gates of Zion,
Far beyond the starry sky."

Mrs G told me all this later, and I would have been embarrassed if I'd known at the time she had heard me like that. She said she'd closed her eyes and smiled. "No stutter at all!" She said I'd brought something new to the house, for which she was grateful. Rather than disturb me, she'd gone quietly into the parlour and sat listening to all the verses. When I reached the final chorus, I'd sung the words of the final line slowly but firmly, then paused for a few seconds and started all over again she told me.

I wish Mrs G had been my real mother.

(But Mrs G's friend Mabel might not have approved. Mabel was religious. It was her life. She should approve of hymn singing. But nowadays she was becoming strange. In her household singing was frowned upon. Silence was the Spirit of her Age. Singing was drawing attention to oneself, and her aim was to abolish the Self. Abolish free thought. Give up one's personality completely. Become a blank sheet of paper.

Mrs G was worried about her old friend Mabel. She had been ill before, but now she was becoming even stranger).

The Full Mabel
The Garden and The Healing

<hr>

(So far, the visitors tend to be respectfully impressed but now start to be a bit sceptical about what I tell them, as it seems so far-fetched. Yet the Panaceans do seem to have genuinely believed the unbelievable. Visitors are all still intrigued, but starting to be dubious about giving unconditional respect).

OK. So let's carry on ….

This building we are in was originally a Boarding House for the boys of Bedford School, and as you can see the garden is quite large. Mabel believed this was the site of the original Garden of Eden, and eventually she declared that the land within a twelve mile radius from here, The Royal Domain, was a special area she protected from Evil. Their garden was different from the straight lines you see here nowadays. They protected it as much as possible from outsiders by having high hedges and fences that couldn't be seen over easily. It's a lovely peaceful place, but not quite what you'd think an original Eden was like.

To the left it opens out to join the garden of number 11 Newnham Road, The Haven. You can see the large Weeping Ash tree, called Yggdrasil, the tree of Life and Knowledge in Norse mythology. The Panaceans thought the tree stood at the centre of the world. You can also see Mabel's end-terrace house, with its garden opened out into the other two, and this is where they had their Garden Parties on the lawn, being served food and drink by the servants. Together, the buildings made up what they called The Campus, where they met and worked every day, and prayed at night in their chapel.

At the side of the chapel a room has details of the activity that made them well known internationally, the Healing Mission. The way it came about was apparently that one day in 1921 a tablet tried to run away from Mabel. Seriously, what happened was that she was about to take a tablet, when it slipped out of her hand, and kept moving away when she tried to grab it. Mabel decided that God must be telling her there was no need to take tablets so she said a prayer over a glass of water and decided that drinking the blessed water was enough to cure illnesses from then on. Other followers took to drinking water she had blessed, and reported that they were feeling better. No medical proof was ever found to show the process worked, but if believers believed and were cured, then surely it must be true. In 1926, the Society Mabel had created was renamed The Panacea Society (meaning the cure for everything) whereas beforehand it had called itself the Community of the Holy Ghost. At the same time it became a registered charity.

After a while, it was clear that this slow but sure healing process was too awkward to benefit people who lived away from the Bedford Headquarters. A system was devised whereby Mabel would breathe her holy breath onto card, and later on large pieces of linen, and pray over them. They would be cut into small squares, and it was held that if a believer put a square into ordinary water and said certain words then drinking it or washing in it would produce a healing effect. These sections of linen could therefore be used by anyone anywhere in the world. In early 1924 this Healing Mission was advertised in newspapers, and very soon there were enormous numbers of people asking to be cured. To keep the Society in relative obscurity, a London address was used rather than have hordes of people turn up at Headquarters. Naturally, when some people claimed they were cured, the whole business shot up like a rocket (but didn't fall like the stick). Requests were received from all over the world. It was all done for free. They refused payment and did not actively try to recruit more members from the Healing Mission.

A very efficient Healing Department was set up under Hilda Green, using several members with good knowledge of foreign languages. Applicants would firstly be sent leaflets about the Society, and when they replied would then be sent instructions on how to use the linen. They had to report back on progress to the Healing Dept (or C.S.S.

as it was known) and might be given advice if they weren't getting better at first. Full details of correspondence was kept on cards. The Healing Dept was wound up in the early 2000's when it was clear that the whole Society was about to become defunct. Overall, about 130,000 people had applied, with most from Britain, USA, the West Indies and Commonwealth/Empire countries. There are masses of letters confirming how the linen had cured believers – there's even one where the person reports that his lumbago is much better now, and by the way, his cows are producing far more milk.

If you read the letters received in the early 2000's, you can't help but feel sorry for the applicants. Typical examples are teenage boys who say they are embarrassed to talk to girls but desperately want to – can the Healing help? Or people with what nowadays we would call OCD – having to wash their hands half a dozen times before they go out. Or people who are clearly suffering from clinical depression, desperately wanting someone or something to show them the way to a happier life. They are all sad people who deserved pity and help.

(But there are ones that are funny. In 1961, the Society Council discussed what to do with a complaining letter from a Mr Hey, who had been using the Healing for 16 years, but was still bald.

How to prepare the Linen was kept as a secret, known only to two people at any one time.

Although the claims to cure anything from lumbago to earache were unlikely, it was only the claim to cure cancer that was ever struck off the list of things that could be zapped.

It's also interesting that as time passed, members seemed to conveniently forget that the linen was only capable of healing because Mabel had breathed her holy breath on it. In 1960 the Council discussed buying more linen as they thought the stock was running out, and decided to find out if any top quality linen was available. It isn't clear whether they went ahead and bought any or not, but the point is that at that meeting no one said that any new linen might not work, as Mabel had died 26 years before! At that meeting was Peter Rasmussen, one of her most loyal followers, and someone who had known her well. Yet he sat and said nothing to point out the illogicality of what was being discussed.

It is easy to snigger at the thought of people being cured of illnesses by pieces of linen, but as very many were helped in this way surely it should be applauded. I'm sure that nowadays doctors prescribe placebo drugs, which may also produce improvements in health in a similar way.

By the way, did you know that in the Andes, they believed that guinea pigs had healing powers? Yes, that's funny, but if it works, and doesn't harm anyone, let's not knock it).

The enormous success of the Healing made the Society well known nationally and internationally. Next, I'll tell you about 24 Bishops and a box.

Etholle
Sitting At The Roundabout

Time passed. You can't hear it or see it, but it does. Faster than you realise. It passes and it passes and it passes. But who knows where it goes?

Mrs G liked me for my openness and optimism. Facile Optimism she called it, and I just nodded and pretended I understood. She said I shouldn't tell people what I guessed they wanted to hear, but say what I really thought, and I decided that was good advice which I tried to follow from then on. I had my faults of course, but I was growing into a role as her companion. Mrs G would ask me to accompany her to shops in the town, to look for clothes, and asked for my ideas (never calling it advice) on the workings of the household. She sometimes deliberately chose things other than the one I preferred, just to show she was in charge I think, even if secretly she agreed with my reasoning. We generally walked everywhere, strolling along Castle Road and stopping to sit on a bench at the junction with Rothsay Road.

The roads had been built in the 1880's, and as this was a place for luxurious houses, the roads were designed to make them even more desirable. At this junction were some of the largest properties and so the owners were given not just their own gardens, but another garden to view for free, set in the large roundabout in the middle of the junction. There was very little traffic so you could stroll from either of the main roads across to the roundabout where there were flowers, young trees, and wooden seats. Later, someone told me this was the first roundabout in the country! This was a meeting place for nannies, parking their high carriages while they chatted in the fresh air. Mrs G pretended that she needed a rest before going further, so we would sit quietly in the sun. I really liked to sit there in silent contact with my companion, staring at the houses surrounding us. One house in particular I liked, for no reason, but when getting to sleep at night I sometimes thought of how good it might be to live there, in large rooms, with servants perhaps. One day she got me to carry her Welsh harp to the roundabout and we sat there with her playing lovely music, with her eyes closed. Some people stopped and listened for a while and even said Thank You, but others just walked on, nose in the air. It was beautiful - not as if it was bagpipes! She would do that from time to time, but didn't tell me how she had learnt to play or why she wanted to play it in public.

It was interesting and sometimes funny sitting there at the roundabout watching the passers-by. Aren't people funny! And isn't Life strange! I remember one day we saw two men walk towards each other and made to shake hands. The taller man held his hand low down, but the smaller man held his very high...the first man realised his mistake and then put his hand higher, but the second man did the same but the other way around, pushing his hand lower. They then did this a third time, so from where we were sitting it looked like they were standing facing each other waving their right hands up and down at each other's stomach. We both burst out laughing, but the taller man looked embarrassed. As they went away, the shorter man grinned at us and waved his hand up and down again to himself. I never saw him again, but I reckon he must have been a nice person to know.

One morning, Mrs G had trouble walking as her foot had a terrible pain and it wouldn't go away, even after several weeks. It was wotcha call giving her gyp. The doctors decided it was a trapped nerve, which might go away eventually ....or might not. In any event, from then on she didn't know from one day to the next whether she would be able to walk pain-free or whether she would have to sit at home or need my help to get anywhere she needed to go to. She visited her friend in Albany Road some evenings as well as two afternoons each week, and although she said nothing about this, she always seemed on edge afterwards. As she couldn't walk well she needed me to push her there in a rickety contraption on wheels, a throwback to the time she herself had briefly used it to push her husband about before his death. We would stop a few yards from the door of number 12 and she would get herself out, struggle to the door, and tell me to come back at a certain time and wait for her. She told me I should not knock on the door. At the end of the road I would look back and see a small figure in her flowery hat too tall to look elegant welcomed into the building by a servant. I might hear noise from the garden next door, a gap where you would expect number 10 to be. The noise of boys playing.

One evening, Mrs G stumbled as she went to Mrs Barltrop's door, and I rushed back to help. The door opened and a woman let us both in straight away. I did speak, but it was like trying to get a reply from an angler. She looked at me as if she had been trying to eat vinegar with a fork and spoon. I was embarrassed by the silence and to be inside the house so I stood with hunched shoulders, looking back through the glass of the door out into the road, thinking that I would be told off for being somewhere I shouldn't. After a few muttered conversations between two women, who ignored me, Mrs G said I should wait in the back garden until she had finished her business there.

The garden was quite small, as the property was just a modest terraced house. On one side there was a house similar to this one. On the other, a wall divided Number 12 from what I later learnt was a large building used as a Boarding House for boys of Bedford School. I could see a lovely large copper coloured tree next to the looming mass of the building, and could hear shouts from what seemed to be tennis players on the other side. At the bottom of the garden a dilapidated shed blocked the view of another large building next to the Boarding House. In its grounds was another interesting tree of a kind I had never seen before.

After a while, I remember being ushered back into the house to where Mrs G was waiting. I glanced through an open door into a room on the left side, where several silent women were sitting, looking towards another woman who was standing near the French Door. They were clearly paying her all their attention. The servant opened the front door and Mrs G fell into the chair, indicating to me that I should now push her back home. The door shut behind us, and cheerily I said "Home James, and don't spare the bike." I don't know where I had come up with such a stupid expression, but it was useful to break the ice.

Mrs G said nothing to me on the way home but from time to time said things to herself.

" Drivel...Gibberish...Mumbo Jumbo."

I loved that word, Drivel, and tried to use it in normal conversations from then on, but it wasn't easy. It's hard to bring it into a conversation without sounding rude.

The Full Mabel
The Box

(For the First Time Visitor, much of what they find out is new to them, and it amazes them, but some of them have a vague recollection from somewhere about the next bit and it is quite a show-stopper when we go into the Box room. In all the building, this is the room where they tend to ask the most questions, and some of them sense a "spirit" in the place. Yes, it is very evocative, but personally the only room that gives me a slight tingle down the spine is Dilys' room in the last part of the museum that we go to, so more about that in a bit...).

Mabel became frustrated at living so close to this building, as the boys in the schoolhouse made too much noise for her liking. Rachel Fox records that at times Mabel was completely fed up with the noise from boys playing tennis, and 3 pianos being played at once.

(Mabel didn't like unnecessary noise. She didn't like servants humming or singing, or neighbours with "particularly trying" voices. When she courteously asked the school staff to quieten down, they refused, "with uncalled for indifference and hardness," which made her worse. The boys had plagued her with their noise since 1916, she said. In 1923, she also complained that Satan and Lucifer were both working against her via the the loud singing of a thrush which for 7 years "has systematically sung its loudest into my bedroom window, to awaken me at three and four in the morning, making further sleep impossible for some hours." She had a long list of things she disapproved of).

In 1930 they bought the school building – which solved the noise pollution problem. One member in particular was very generous in giving money to buy it. He must have been a very devoted follower or perhaps a bit too trusting or simple; I think Mabel liked that in a man. This building was set out and equipped for a very special purpose – it was prepared for the opening of Joanna Southcott's Box of Prophecies.

You'll remember that Southcott had died in 1814, leaving many followers, a box, but no baby Shiloh. In the century after her death followers kept her sealed box safe and unopened. As one custodian died or became too old for the responsibility, it was then kept by another Southcottian. At the start of the twentieth century there was a renewed interest in Southcott and her box, with the headmistress of a girls' school, Alice Seymour, reprinting all Southcott's books, something that produced interest in Britain and around much of the world. In 1914, Mabel read a pamphlet about Southcott and it was probably this that started the Panacea Society ball rolling. At about the same time, Ellen Oliver was in touch with Helen Shepstone, a South African spiritualist, who had her own interest in the box.

There were strict conditions for the box to be opened, the main one being that it must happen in the presence of 24 Bishops of the Church of England, and only after due ceremonies and rigmaroles including the Bishops reading all of Southcott's books. Shepstone, Fox and Seymour in their different ways contacted the Archbishop of Canterbury, asking him to get his Bishops together for it to be opened. Separately, Mabel was also asking for the same thing. The Archbishop rejected the requests, and it was probably this, rather than worry about the safety of her son Eric in the war, that tipped Mabel over the edge and meant she landed up in a Northampton mental institution in late April 1915.

A few years later, the early Panaceans spent immense energy and time campaigning for the box to be opened. They put adverts in national newspapers, they handed out leaflets, they got people to sign petitions. They spoke at public meetings – Alice Jones in particular spoke often at Hyde Park Speakers' Corner, and spoke well. Posters advised that London was in peril. War, Disease, Crime, Banditry and Perplexity would increase unless the box was opened. The first petition in 1924, with 10,000 signatories, was rejected. Alice Seymour put distance between herself and the Panaceans as their campaign was too blunt for her liking. A second great petition had some 30,000 signatures, but by the time it was presented in 1935, Mabel was dead.

Despite the rejections this building, which is now the main part of the museum, was prepared for 24 Bishops to stay, in suitable luxury, for the opening of the box .....tomorrow, the next day, sometime, never. Each Bishop would have a bedroom, but they would share two bathrooms. There were very comfortable furnishings, and everything a Bishop could possibly want or need. They had rehearsals for the great day, and improvements were often made to the details. Sketch plans of who should sit where in the Box Room were made. At one point Mabel suddenly decided that they had to find additional room in the front row for "six Jews of repute," so they had to buy more chairs.

The room and building was never used for the intended purpose as the box was never opened, but opportunists used the free publicity to take advantage, and other rival boxes appeared. One box was owned by a fraudster named Harry Price, who also owned Borley Rectory, "The most Haunted House in England," which just happened to accidentally burn down when he was about to be exposed. He and other fraudsters tried to use the Panaceans' national profile for their own ends, but the other boxes were clearly fakes. For the second time in History, Joanna Southcott became a figure of ridicule, with cartoons poking fun at the idea of it being a serious phenomenon. The Panaceans probably lost hope that it would ever be opened, but the national advertising carried on right up until the 1990's.

(It surprises people that the Panaceans put such enormous time and effort into their campaigns and setting Castleside up for the opening of the Box, yet they didn't actually have it anyway. It wasn't until 1957 that they became guardians of the box, when the Southcottian who had it died and it was decided that there was no suitable Southcottian any more so it should go to the most suitable alternative – The Panacea Society.

It's also surprising that even when they had the Box, it was not publicised to the membership, with just a few members being aware that the precious thing their founder had always wanted had now come to the Garden of Eden.

The Box is held in a safe place in Bedford, I understand, and recent photos exist, but I've never seen it myself. I don't see how the Box can ever be opened, or even be X-rayed either.

It was put into the custodianship of the Panacea Society, which no longer exists, by a particular group of Southcottians, who no longer exist, and is now held by the Panacea Trust, which does not have any specific instructions on what its duties are in connection with the Box, apart presumably from keeping it safe. Morally, the Trust would have to follow the wishes of the original Southcottian owners, who specified all the various conditions for it to be opened, including the very unlikely possibility of 24 Bishops turning up for a few days in Bedford. Most visitors are pleased that the mystery of the Box will carry on).

Faces- 12 Albany Road Bedford
Jan 1920

The hallway was dark. The only light was from candles. The rooms were always dark and gloomy at the best of times, but even though someone had tried their best by lighting candles on every available desk or table, the corridor looked like it was leading to some cellar or dungeon or prison from which people were less likely to escape than to rot. An oubliette in a Victorian terraced house.

On the right side, the Parlour and the Dining room had been made into one bigger room by opening wide the connecting dark wooden doors. Chairs were set out so that all present could see the woman at the end. And she herself had an even better view of them. The candle on the small table in front of her threw flickering warm light up onto her face, then the shadows moved up to make shapes on the ceiling, moving erratically as she made even the slightest movement. All those present, her congregation, were sitting in silence, hands folded, heads bowed. Still. No movement. As it should be.

The women could almost be identical – small and intense, closed and obedient.

Vicar's wife....curate's daughter ....widow....spinster....suffragette ....vicar's widow...frustrated politician ....frustrated activist ....bluestocking....Truth seeker ...widow...sisters...sisters ...
All were followers.
Clever woman ....good administrator ...kind woman ....good orator
... naif ...dogsbody...harsh mistresses ...old friends ....well-off ... Expectants

Followers.

Gertrude...Ellen...Kate...Bessie...Alice...Kate ...Hilda... Winna.

God had spoken to her in her trance, and she had now told her followers his words. She had performed the service. Now, in turn, she washed the feet of her apostles as her brother had done with his followers. His were men; hers were women.

The ecstasy over, they all stood, and their smiles made the room light and warm.

Upstairs, a 90 year old aunt was ill, and a 21 year old daughter called Dilys stared blankly at her bedroom wall.

Downstairs, some exchanged presents. Alice embraced Kate. Gertrude embraced Ellen. Ellen gazed at Octavia.

In their way, they were happy.

Etholle
One Way

It must have been at about that time I started to think about the goings on with Mrs Barltrop. I can remember things more clearly from then onwards – the secrecies, the strangeness and the skulduggery. Delyth Gwynne, that's Mrs G to you, went a bit quiet and strange for a couple of days after her little upset, and really was ill. Just stared into space and didn't eat. I looked after her of course, but then I was ill myself, with pneumonia.

Mrs G was on the ball, and had me taken to the hospital before things got too serious, but for a few days I had a fever and didn't know what I was doing or where I was. Gradually I felt better, and was able to see the other women in the hospital ward. Some patients were ill, some were good tidy ill, some were wotcha call ill, and the worst were hully ill. One old lady in particular, at the end of the room, seemed to be in a really bad way and the curtains were normally closed. Her relations were always around her, fussing about. They looked far too well educated and well off to be in such a poor place as this. Mrs G came to see me once but no one else came, as I didn't know anyone apart from the people I'd chatted to in the streets. Anyway, on the day I was to leave, the smartly dressed man who I'd worked out was the son of the old lady at the end of the room, walked up to my bed and just stood there.

"Did you realise that last night you were singing at the top of your voice? At two o'clock! You were singing while the patients were trying to sleep."

I was upset about that. I'd always found that the best way to finish the day was to sing a good hymn or two, and if I woke up in the middle of the night then I'd sing another few more. To myself of course, but I must have forgotten where I was and as my ears aren't quite the full ticket I must have been extra loud. I said I was truly sorry for disturbing his mother. "No, don't worry about it. You see, we were here last night, around the bed as my mother was dying. She had been in a bad way, and we were just hoping that her last moments would be peaceful. Then all of a sudden we heard a voice from nowhere singing hymns. She smiled, and I suppose she thought that she was going up to Heaven, and there was an angel singing to help her on her way. It was lovely. Thank you. It was perfect."

Well, what a turn up for the books! I'd done something good. That really made me feel better. I was an angel, and I hadn't even known it. A simple-hearted girl like me. Isn't Life strange …

Anyway, after I got back Mrs G was pleased about that little story and asked me to sing that hymn to her. I couldn't remember which one it had been, probably "O God our help in ages past," so I thought I'd sing one of my favourites, a jolly one :

"This is my story, this is my song,
Praising my Saviour all the day long;
This is my story, this is my song,
Praising my Saviour all the day long.

Perfect submission, all is at rest,
I in my Saviour am happy and blest,
Watching and waiting, looking above,
Filled with His goodness, lost in His love"

Mrs G even clapped her hands she was so pleased. There was something different about her, as if she had decided to trust me in things that she knew about. I don't know why but perhaps it made her feel better to get things off her chest. So she told me about her friend Mabel.

Well, did she have a lot to say! She was a good, honest person, so I've no reason to question what she said. Her husband had always believed that you could judge a person by what they said, what they did, what others said about them, and of course, the company they kept. By that way of looking at her Mabel was a bit of a conundrum, but Mrs G tried to think of her when she was at her kindly best, rather than the figure she had now become. "She's taken on a jacobite load. She has hopes and dreams that have become so real and essential to her that she can't accept any criticism. It is like being on the wrong train, on a train that is going faster and faster, and when you realise that you are going in the wrong direction you find any reason you can to convince yourself that everyone else is on the wrong train, but you are in the Right. She and her new friends seem to think that if they pray loudly enough then the train will somehow arrive at the place they hoped, and if any outsider points out the truth, they turn their backs and ignore them." I thought that was a clever comparison.

About that time I started to notice Mrs G's clever little comments about goings on, and how she often said things that could be taken two ways. She was very sarcastic though people didn't realise it. We got to know how to communicate with each other without talking. She might say something to someone and I'd notice that she raised her left eyebrow and that was a sign that she really thought the opposite of what she had said. Or if she wanted me to rescue her from someone who was irritating her she would somehow wag her ears without touching them. I realised that she was funny as well as clever and someone with integrity.

I once told her that I thought she was very clever, but she quickly said that in the Land of the Blind the One-Eyed Man is King, and so perhaps she was nothing special really.

She told me about how they had met when the Barltrops had moved to Bedford in 1905, and the two clerics had talked about religious matters, with the wives in another room talking practical things, watching Mrs Barltrop's two youngest children playing. Mrs Barltrop often overheard the talk of the men, and made comments to Mrs G about what they said. It seemed to Mrs G that what Mrs Barltrop said made very good sense, and she got the impression that had she been a man she would have become someone who was someone. When alone with her, she was someone who hooked you in and "got" you and made you feel you were the only and most important person in the world, that she was someone you felt you must never ever let down, and you genuinely felt in the company of someone from another better place and you were a better person for being with her. Mrs G loved to see young Dilys playing with her dog in the road outside, teaching it to sit, shake hands and roll over. Sometimes she felt sorry for her though, as the little girl would often stop what she was doing and just stare into space. Mrs G would find some excuse to ask her to do some small job or ask what she thought about so and so or put her arm round her shoulders.

When her husband died, Mrs Barltrop's public face was that of a brave woman, looking after her four children with small resources. But in private she was inconsolable, she staggered about like the survivor of a train wreck, her face was whitewashed blank. Her body shook for no reason and worst of all, she could get no comfort from the one place that should have offered it; when she went to church, she had attacks of panic which she could hardly control. Often when Mrs G went to see her, she would just sit and stare into space, hands folded on her lap, unable to do anything. She cut off her long hair to show her grief. The children seemed to be very quiet and accepting of what had happened but Mrs G held that they had to be cared for properly, and with the help of Arthur's sister Lennie Bull who lived nearby, they decided they should look after the family while Mrs Barltrop went into the Three Counties Asylum for treatment for the depression she clearly had. Lennie had always got on well with her, and Mrs Barltrop had helped Lennie with her daughter Rita when Lennie had lost her first husband years before. They trusted each other.

Things worked out well, and when she came back home, the household was on a fairly stable footing thanks to the support given by Lennie and Mrs G, and the financial help from Mrs Barltrop's aunt Fanny who gave her worldly advice to the family, though by now illness made her immobile.

"The youngsters only needed a bit of kind attention and to know someone will be there for a nice cuddle" Mrs G reckoned, and I think she must have been on the right track there. When I was being moved from one place to another before I came here, it didn't matter whether the people were nice or less nice to me – all I wanted was for them to be interested in me and to know where I could go when I felt sad or uncertain.

"Life carried on" said Mrs G, "and Mabel carried on with her interest in all things theological, writing to all sorts of people about all sorts of obscure ideas and beliefs and to my mind not spending enough time with her children. Oh yes, she loved them right enough, but seemed to forget about them when her mind was concentrating on her writing and correspondence. "Little Flower" she called Dilys and it was lovely to see them together. But she was getting obsessed with the religious study, constantly disagreeing and battling with some theologian or another and fighting battles she could never win because she was a woman. She wrote things under the pseudonym of a man so people would take her more seriously. I tried to see her as much as possible, so did Lennie and Rita, but when we went round to see her and have a cup of tea she would go off in a world of her own, babbling on about some writer who had irritated her and was obviously in the wrong. Dilys was a young girl of a delicate age, who found it hard to bring friends home from school to meet her mother because it might be embarrassing. How could a teenage girl say to her friends: Do you want to come and have tea at my house today? You can meet my mother. She's the Daughter of God, you know? She realised her mother wasn't the same as other people, but felt she couldn't be nasty to her.

The war came, and Eric went away; but although she was so so proud of him, keeping boxes of photos of him in his uniform, she was more interested in Religion. She told me more than once that she heard messages from Arthur, and started saying he had been more than just a cleric - *My Chevalier*, she called him. The real obsession started in about 1914, after she read about a woman called Joanna Southcott, who had died a hundred years before, leaving prophecies in a sealed box, never to be opened except in certain circumstances of great unrest in the world. She thought if the box were to be opened then Christ might return to earth for a new millennium as promised in the Book of Revelation.

Poppycock, I say. Very fanciful. She just wanted something to believe in, and that was definitely not what the Bible said and my husband tried to tell her. She kept writing to the Church asking for the Archbishop to make his Bishops open the Box, but it was like hitting her head against a brick wall and she got depressed and strange again. My husband tried as much as he could to make her see sense, but her mind was closed. We decided I should keep as friendly as possible because although she was thinking nonsense she and the family might need help again if her illness came back. Lennie felt the same, and was appalled at some of the piffle she came out with and in the end we gently persuaded her to go into St Andrews Hospital in Northampton in April 1915. We made her believe it was completely voluntary, but believe you me it was necessary and would have been forced on her if it had gone on much longer. She never forgave Lennie, but for some reason she confided in me that she was grateful for my help in getting her there as it helped her find her way. The doctors told Lennie and me that for a time she was depressed and perhaps a danger to herself, and although we didn't tell the children this, they suspected it I think."

Mrs G told me all this and I listened, all ears, as she told me more and more. People often said I was a good listener and I think that's a good asset to have. Later on, when I listened in on the conversations at the Annual Meetings I noticed that some people, like Major Carew-Hunt, could only listen to anyone for about two sentences before he would jump in with his fourpennyworth, which I think is rude. He never interrupted Mrs Goodwin though.

Anyway, Mrs G carried on telling me all the details of how Mrs Barltrop had been for the next year and a half till she came out. She had been physically ill in hospital, but had eventually stopped being depressed and a danger to herself. But then she started having more voices telling her things; she heard voices from God, Arthur and other people. She decided she had a great mission chosen for her by God, and had voluntarily gone into hospital to help her nerves and to investigate reforms that needed to be made to inmates in mental hospitals, not that she was an inmate! When she came out she wasn't the same person that Mrs G had known and once loved being with. Officially she was well enough to go home but from then on Mrs G only saw glimpses of the old Mabel. Instead, the new Mabel was still prone to panic attacks, delusions and inexplicable routines and habits that she had to keep to or else something bad would happen to her. The strangest one was that very soon she decided she must never walk more than 77 steps from her house, or else Satan would get her. Her state of mind wasn't helped when Eric was killed in France. It must have been awful for Dilys in particular to see her mother in such a confused and strange state of mind and incapable of giving a normal loving home to her children, instead giving her attention to her mission. She was still unwell physically, and for ever afterwards maintained that this was a necessary burden she had to bear for her mission to be achieved. Like Christ, she too had to suffer.

Mrs G had had enough at this point, and I suggested we go and sit at the roundabout in Rothsay Road to take the air. I needed fresh air as well as I hadn't realised how strange a friend Mrs Barltrop was to her, although in a way she was still loyal to her. Mrs G was loyal, but not obsessed, whereas it sounded like Mrs Barltrop's followers were almost hypnotised into thinking ridiculous thoughts.

Now I realised why Mrs G occasionally went into deep silent thought and then muttered words like "Drivel" and "Gibberish" to herself.

As we sat on the seat watching the occasional passer-by, we were facing the house that I had for a long time imagined I might live in one day, the house on the corner, number 19. We sat in silence, but it was the kind of silence between two people content to be in each other's company where no words are needed for there to be communication. I wondered why Mrs G liked me – perhaps she mistook my age. I had always found that I got on with people of all ages, as older people took me as being older than I was and younger ones thought I was their age. Now, in the summer of 1920, I was seventeen going on forty as far as she was concerned and treated as a proper adult. My time in her house had helped me grow up and she thought me more sensible than some of the real adults she rubbed shoulders with.

I noticed Frank the chimney-sweep going to No 19, and waved to him. I loved seeing the brush come out of the top of the chimney and wobble about when he came to Mrs G's house from time to time. After she died, I still had him come to sweep the chimneys, and he told me that he charged different rates for people, depending on how nice and friendly they were, and I thought that was very kind of him, especially as he hardly charged anything at all in the first place. For the poorest people he only asked for a cup of tea and a piece of cake. Mrs G tapped me on the knee and carried on.

Her visits to see Mabel (I now thought I could use her Christian name, as I almost knew her) had become something to dread rather than a chance to catch up with a welcoming friend. The house buzzed with women she hardly knew, who didn't seem completely normal. Mabel swung from the wonderfully empathetic friend she knew to "a fervent shaman giving instructions to obedient followers who clearly idolised her." I associated the word shaman with tales of Africa, as I had seen pictures and loved tales about the Whirling of the Dervishes, and imagined Mabel and her followers performing in the garden of her house.

Mrs G told me about Ellen Oliver, who had moved to Bedford to be near Mabel, and had willingly followed instructions to have her two magnificent Persian cats put down when she came; Mabel had ordered that pets could be disruptive in the Community, and were not allowed. Some of the women, especially Ellen, seemed to be too keen on giving Mabel presents, as if they wanted to be in favour with their leader. Even Mrs Firth, who was well known to Mrs G, had lost her natural Common Sense, and now seemed to treat Mabel as a divine figure, and Mabel was doing nothing to stop all this nonsense. Ellen, who skipped from one hare-brained idea to another, had brought several of her friends to Bedford as well, all of whom also seemed to be sleepwalking or daydreaming. Mrs G told me she gradually found out that Mabel thought she was a great prophet, Shiloh, and she was referred to by her followers as Octavia. She had appointed Apostles and was working to prepare the world for the day of Revelation. She sighed and lifted her arms high in the air:

" She's not the Messiah. She's just a very silly woman."

She had held services in her house, "with a handkerchief on her head, would you believe!" and had washed the feet of her followers. She performed all sorts of mumbo-jumbo with the Oath of Homage to Jesus Christ, and the Service of the Crowning, whatever that was. She said that God was a four sided thing – there was God the Father, his son Jesus, his daughter Mabel/Octavia and the Divine Mother (formerly the Holy Spirit). The Divine Mother was the eternal feminine aspect of God, which had been missing in the world for so long, and she was to bring about its acceptance worldwide. Mabel had messages from God each day, which she then passed on to the followers, and to cap it all, she gave the impression that she thought her late husband Arthur had in fact been a second incarnation of Jesus. Followers had to work towards becoming fully "sealed" members and had to comply with the Community Ordinances and Doctrines. Included in the Ordinances was the instruction that they must believe they will not die, they must save up money to establish Heaven on Earth, and that believing the word of anyone other than people that she herself had previously instructed was foolishness. In other words, She Knew Best and Must Be Obeyed. She decreed that members should live in Community houses or "nests" where she could gather her "young"and they must all purify themselves to prepare for the Great Day. Her word was to be absolute, and in the event of anyone rebelling against her authority, they would be suspended from the daily service and if necessary, would be expelled from the Community. The words were intended to frighten nervous people into accepting her authority. She wanted to get 144,000 full members, and was now hopeful of getting there as her Healing Mission was becoming well-known all over the world.

All this time I listened quietly and nodded my head every so often.

"I'm not a member, but a Lay Member, which means I have agreed to make our house available to entertain visitors, housing new arrivals temporarily, lending furniture and generally helping out in the more mundane things. There are so many visitors arriving that they can hardly cope. This madness is growing, like flowers in the Spring. I've done this so that we both can be involved in the Society, but not be proper members. In that way I hope to keep an eye on what is going on, and step in to help if and when things go completely wrong. This is a mess, but we've got to try and make sense of it all." She sounded completely serious, I could tell. And with that, she upped and walked home, briefly turning round to me and saying "Sorry, Etholle, but you are a good person and I know I can rely on you. You may have obligations as well, even if you aren't aware of them."

DoG- 1920

The Daughter of God sat in the front room of her house, 12 Albany Road. Her home. The place where they all congregated. The centre of the Community. Her Community. The centre of the world. Near the Tree. The Garden of Eden.

They had all come to her. To Shiloh. To Octavia. To the messiah. Not Mabel, but the Daughter of God. She was their leader. She had to carry out her duties.

Nervously, she got up and walked to the window. Her prison. 77 steps: no more. She could see through the net curtain, see down the road, see up the road. She touched the piano, so comfortingly clean and polished. Lifted the lid. Closed the lid. Looked back to the window. She again sat down at the table in the middle of the room. She touched the Bible, open as always. The chair; a gift for Arthur from the Dover Band of Hope. A good man. But more. Much more. She looked up at the white declaration on the wall, framed so that it drew attention to itself. Her son. Her eldest son. Dead. Shot down from the skies, in uniform. Proudly she remembered how proud he looked in the photographs. But Pride is a sin, and he died. A good son, though never a member. Never acknowledged her as the messiah. He himself would have been God's grandson, but was shot down. Much better if that space on the wall had been a letter from an Archbishop.

She walked past the mirror.
>To the Aspidistra.
>>Looked back at the table.
>>At the writing desk.

Back to the wall.
Only 77 steps were allowed to her.
It did sadden her, but her son's death wasn't the biggest sadness of that time.

Her time in the asylum.

The madness. No, she had just been let down.

The foolish Archbishop. Why couldn't he see the truth of her mission? God's will had been ignored. The blinkered eyes of the Church had held back The Day. It had brought her to absolute despair. Bunyan's hero would himself have given up. Castle Despair.

But her time there had not been wasted.

She had seen things. Heard things. Learnt things.

The Truth. The Way Ahead.

To Heaven on Earth.

She sat at the table.

77 steps: no more.

Silence.

The room was growing dark.

She switched on the lamp. Too bright.

She switched off the lamp.

Her duties must be carried out. The others knew nothing of her sufferings. The duties tired her out. She stood up.

Touched her Bible.

There was hope, though. Her apostles had been active. More followers. More work for her secretary to do, communicating her work to people in far off towns and beyond the seas. Sincere followers, the right sort, with proper manners as well as beliefs. Jessie Johnson was right – Bedford was truly the place of God's Glory.

But Jessie's ideas had been presumptuous. Heaven could not be a park studded with jewels. She was gone now. Too presumptuous, though she had worked hard and had brains. But her ideas were unwelcome.

She touched the Bible. Stroked it. Stood up. Paused, then picked up a letter from the table and smiled. The smile of a teacher seeing

the work of a good pupil. This was what gave her hope – seeing her work achieve results. New members. New followers. More believers gathering.
Some in the town scoffed.
No, most people scoffed.
They were beyond help.
She was safe in her world, with her followers. Her believers.
The Lord would come. It must be soon. She must work to make it soon. She must be tireless. She was the Daughter Of God.
She didn't like to write this down. She had once done so, daydreaming, and Kate had pointed out that she had absent-mindedly highlighted the letters D O and G. DOG. And God was Dog backwards. What did this mean? A cruel joke. Followers of Satan would laugh and ridicule.

She had seen off Satan before, that summertime, running to the North East corner of the room, pointing her finger at him, and laughing scornfully at him."The daughter of Zion hath despised thee. The daughter of Jerusalem hath shaken her finger at thee!"
She looked in the mirror.

She had once been a handsome woman, now made haggard by devotion to her religious passion. She suffered that others might see the way to Heaven. They must follow her. Her duty. There was no question about it. The Bible was clear. She was the Shiloh. She was Octavia. God told her, every day. The scripts were clear. Gave instruction on the way ahead. They came every day. Always on time. He was always ready for her, like a devoted father setting out time to help and perfect a favourite daughter. It was undeniable. She was his daughter. He was guiding her. Had always guided her. Would always guide her path until the glorious day when there would be peace and earthly happiness forever. The Bible said so. It would be soon, if only the Bishops could be made to come.
She stared out of the window, closed her eyes, breathed in slowly.

Breathed out. Opened her eyes. Looked down at the Bible, open at the beginning of the book of Revelation.

She started to read, and with each passing moment and verse her breathing became calm, her legs and arms slowed their involuntary trembling, and her face became serene and content.

She was the Daughter of God and she was happy.

The Full Mabel
The Flock Grows

(We're near the end of the tour, conveniently ending up at the café, but there's a whole new world to look at before we get there. Sometimes, when we go into Mabel's house, visitors get confused, thinking that this was where the baby Shiloh was going to be born to Mabel, when in fact it was Joanna Southcott who was supposed to give birth to Shiloh, in 1814, years before Mabel herself was born. I sometimes think it might be a good idea to ask them diplomatically phrased questions on the way around just to check they've all got the basics. But it is a lot to take in from one visit).

There's still more of the museum to look at. To start with, there's the bit that isn't open yet, over there across the grass is The Haven, a house not as big as Castleside but luxurious in its time. It's been pretty well derelict for over 50 years now but it will soon be restored and become part of the museum. It was bought by the widow Kate Firth, whose adult son Geoffrey also stayed there from time to time, but she willingly offered it as a large Community House, the place for meetings, parties and important events as well as a place for members to live. It was home for Dilys, the Carew-Hunts and others over the years. Firth and Mabel fell out and for a short period members were barred from the building but before long they bought it back. By the 1960's it was too expensive for the shrinking Community to use as a home so it was in effect put into mothballs. It will be quite something in a few years time.

And here is number 12 Albany Road, with its back garden opened out into the garden of Castleside. It's a fairly modest end-terrace house with an extension at the back. Inside, it's been restored with original furniture to show what it was like in the 1930's. We've now got a small café set up in one of the rooms, and the décor lets you see what it must have felt like here nearly a hundred years ago. Upstairs, Mabel's bedroom is set out as it was on the day she died. Dilys' room was at the back though she eventually lived a nomadic life, moving from one Community house to another. At the front is the bedroom shared by Mabel's aunt Fanny and her nurse, Emily Goodwin. There's a small bedroom for a servant, and another small room that was used for the early services. Over the years many different followers lived here, including Hilda Green and Peter Rasmussen – who lived in the attic. In fact I often wonder how they managed to cram so many people in here as it seems to have had as many lodgers as Ken Barlow's house in Coronation Street. Seriously though, when Mabel's son Adrian came back home with his new family to visit in 1929, he was shocked to find that they couldn't stay in his old family home with his mother and sister as there were so many strangers living there. He compared it with a Boarding House with an unpleasant landlady and the kind of tenants with whom he would not want to associate. Mabel's world revolved around the Society and her work, not her family.

In 1920, as the movement was gathering momentum, two important people joined. Emily Goodwin arrived and soon became the nurse to Mabel's aunt, and Mabel's first memory of Emily was when she dropped a bucket of water down the stairs of Number 12. But she became Mabel's all too essential supporter very soon, despite her working class background. An Australian Dane, Peter Rasmussen, also arrived in 1920. He was a genuinely sincere man looking for spiritual meaning, and he immediately decided Mabel/Octavia was the person to whom he must devote his whole life. Mabel was so impressed by him that he was fully sealed in just over a week. He was a small practical man, shy because of a speech impediment, but he soon became a major figure in the Society because of his great theological knowledge, loyalty to Mabel, and building talents. He single handedly built extensions to Number 12, converted the attic to a bedroom, converted a run-down shed at the bottom of the garden to a liveable "Garden Room," built a fish pond and had other practical projects. If there was ever an Olympic gold medal for Loyalty he would have been a contender, that's for sure. Rightly, Mabel considered him her "Rock." His 'Angelic Name' was Peter Gabriel. Which is nice.

The Garden Room, with windows and door looking out onto the garden of The Haven, was at times a living/sleeping place, a community room, and eventually became the Chapel, where daily services were held. The "Jerusalem Window" was added in 1929, and after Castleside was bought in 1930, a Clock Tower was built, to house "Little Ben." Nowadays, the room at the side of the Chapel is used to show details of The Healing, and just beyond that is the "Wireless Room"which is a representation of what I refer to as their Entertainment Complex. It's just a room with a piano, dart board, radio and other things needed for enjoying simple entertainment. Emily Goodwin gave instructions for a "Wireless" to be bought in 1923 and it was used to listen to important messages such as sermons. I like to think of them sitting here at times, listening to the Shipping Forecast, hearing the names given to the original thirteen water areas that today still take you into a world of comforting fusty nostalgia. They are words that bring a feeling of calm, reassurance and permanence: Shetland, Forties, Humber, Dogger, Wight, Shannon, Clyde, Hebrides and the rest.

So that's a tour of what they called The Campus, or what Rasmussen called "God's Acre," and an idea of the history and main aspects of the Panacea world. I think it would be a good move for you now to have a cup of tea or coffee in the café, manned or womaned more likely, by our excellent volunteers, and mull over what you've seen. Then wander around again to look at things in more detail, and perhaps we can get together to chat about questions and thoughts that you will have. It's a lot to take in and the more you learn the more and more fascinating it all becomes.

You'll also have opinions on what they were like, what they did and what we might think of them. Let's talk about that as well. But whether you think they were sincere, deranged or just strange, let's start with an open mind. And remember: they did little harm.

At The Haven 2016

After years of just sitting there doing nothing, the house is starting to perk up a bit. There are ideas floating around in the air, in the large spaces of the hallway, the landings, and the bedrooms, even in the small room, with the hooks in the ceiling to store meat, and in the rooms that could have been used for God knows what. The well, the bathrooms, the eight bells in the kitchen, to remind the servants what their job was. The two staircases, again to separate those who have from those who have not. The door between the two nations, covered in red velvet, so the lower class would at this point remember to adjust their clothes, their manners and their speech. On the first floor, just a curtain to do the same job. Quieter, so as not to disturb the betters in their sleep. Not quite Downton Abbey, but a smaller, middle class copy of that mentality, and just as wrong .

The rooms are large. Large spaces to enjoy, to own and to idle. Years of neglect though. Cracks in some walls, but nothing serious, all wallpaper stripped off to the plaster, ready for action. Built on the corner of two desirable roads to live in, even the servants have views. Tall trees opposite – a high wind in the wrong direction would be dangerous for the house. A conker tree – there are lots of Horse Chestnut trees in the town. Perhaps, years ago, a kindly man in authority saw children collecting conkers in the Autumn and decided to give generations to come a present from an unknown Father Christmas by having them planted. A simple thing for children to do, that makes them happy. But perhaps the mystery man got even more pleasure from his gift. That goodwill has lasted decades, with more to come.

The Haven: a secure port in a storm. A solid dependable place, safe from outside worries, ills and evils. And next door to the Garden of Eden itself.

A few rooms have old, dark wood furniture, ready to go to the Auction House. Not much of a market for this stuff nowadays, but it will help pay for the renovations. Some rooms have built-in cupboards – state of the art in their day perhaps. Yes, this could be a wonderful place. A real mansion, easily worth seven figures. Now emptied, ready for action, but details yet to be decided. Once a key part of the Panacea Campus, it will be a key part of the Panacea Museum complex. Top floor to be the Archives, and the first floor to be the offices. The ground floor to be the main museum entrance? The shop? The Education Centre? The International Centre of Excellence? The café? Definitely the centre of activity. How to keep the feel of the place but to make it work well in the new role? Lots to be decided, but it will be done well, that's for sure.

The small group looking round the house were all amazed at the magnificent building that it once must have been. Not, however, a home. More of a place to live, with nice things, but not really a home. Nice furniture, nice gardens, nice spaces, but nowhere to have fun, in the way that a large modern family with relaxed attitudes to child rearing might create. A place to run around, wonder at a giant Christmas tree, play hide and seek, make a lot of noise. But it was never like that.

Some touches of individuality though. Some bare walls upstairs have pencil handwriting, in old fashioned style, with messages that aren't clear. On some bare plaster walls there are pencil drawings … of teapots. Initials that might be to show the height of different children at different ages. These will soon be covered up by new wallpaper. Nobody will remember them, apart from the people who carry out the decoration, or who spot the pencil work before the work starts. Why teapots? Weird. Hmm, but there could be an explanation, if you believe in coincidences. Perhaps the result of a visit long ago by a supporter. A lady who half wanted to make her name in the world of ….Teapots. So obsessed that she couldn't help herself drawing them on any available place? Or perhaps not.

No obvious ghosts here, though they might feel at home in the quiet emptiness.

They might look out from the Blue Room, out onto the lawn, where they had joined in with the Garden Parties, the games, the ceremonies of a Time from a different Time. The fine clothes, the starched collars, the cucumber sandwiches served by one nation to another. Polite laughter, stilted conversations, some worried not to seem too open, too familiar, too much wanting to stand out. Someone would be listening. And opposite the window, the looming shape of the locked house. Castleside, No 9 Newnham Road. The house specially prepared for the Great Day. The visiting group knew that the hopes of those who had stared across that lawn 90 years before would end in disappointment. Nothing. Gradually, as those believers grew slower and less reliable in mind and body, they would suspect that their lifetime's beliefs would not be realised and they would themselves go to dust, with no clear afterlife. Perhaps they might decide they themselves were at fault, and as is said to be the way of ghosts, they never rested in peace but instead lived an unending Groundhog Day, wandering about the house, looking out over the lawn, trapped in their sad memories that should have been so perfect.

Sharon locked the door and the group strolled slowly away. She was wearing a pair of striking shoes, decorated with figures of a Señor and his Señorita, perhaps the only such pair for miles around. The shoes hinted at her sense of individuality, and made her happy. And when people were surprised and smiled at them, she smiled her own secret smile. The shoes were made by a firm whose name sounded like "Hellfire."

The ghosts, staring out from their self-imposed prison, might have wondered who had the better kind of happiness.

Etholle
Heavy People

Mrs G told me that I was to become a Lay Associate as well, so I had to meet Mabel to go through the introduction process. I waited in the hall at number 12 Albany Road, arriving a few minutes early for my 10.00 AM appointment. I was told that she had already done a Trojan's amount of work, as she was a night owl, needing hardly any sleep. She wasn't well as she suffered all sorts of pains for the sake of earthly sinners like myself, so I should make allowances for her. So said her assistant, a small woman like a dormouse, peering up from round spectacles, slowly telling me what was necessary then rushing away to do something else as if there wasn't enough time in the day to do all she wanted. Later on I realised she was always hyperactive, working in small bursts, then stopping to recover and rush off again.

She took me into the Front Parlour, where Mabel was sitting in a chair at the round table in the middle of the room. She got up immediately and tilting her head to one side, gave me the kindest and most sincere smile I had ever been given. She realised I was nervous as I tried to stutter out a "Goo..Goo..Good M..M....M..." but didn't interrupt me. I would have hated that. She waited till I had managed to greet her, then stepped towards me, put her hand on my elbow and said softly "Please, Etholle, come and join me in my home, I'm SO pleased you have come." She did this while looking at me with what I immediately though was a maternal expression and made me feel safe. She smelt of roses, as if we were in a garden. I sat two chairs away from what I assumed was her preferred seat, but after a few minutes she got up and sat in the chair next to me, as if she was so interested in what I had to say that she had to sit closer so as not to miss anything I said. I was such an interesting person that she would move to be near me rather than the other way around. Although she sat next to me, she moved her chair so that it faced me and I found myself moving my own chair so that we were face to face. At one point there was a knock at the door and when the dormouse lady was allowed in, to tell Mabel that a very important guest had arrived unexpectedly from America, Mabel waved her away, saying that she would see him later, and that she was so enjoying our chat that the important person could wait. When we carried on, Mabel said "Important eh?" with a raised eyebrow. Then she gave me a crafty wink, a smile, and away we went again. When I stuttered she would let me finish, and always listened to what I said, sometimes repeating back to me what I had said a few minutes before. She made me feel a better person than when I had gone into the room. When I left her, I really did feel as if I was ten feet tall. I knew that she was important, but she made me feel special to her. I felt like a Queen. She made you want to never let her down.

When I left, I called her Octavia.

Afterwards, I was shown round the rest of the house, and saw many ladies working in silence but with animation in various departments doing I don't know what but clearly it was important to them. One brushed past me in the hall, dropped a newspaper, and I accidentally stood on it, holding the folded faces to the floor. For some reason I laughed but she said nothing. The dormouse lady took me to the door, waited until I had gone through the gate, then closed the door. Later, I learnt that members were instructed that it was rude to close the door before a visitor had reached the pavement, but when I looked back to give her a smile and say goodbye she had gone, gone back in as

94

quickly as possible. Such a contrast with how Mabel had treated me.

When I got back I told Mrs G about what a welcoming person Mabel had been."Her claws are in you. Well, you've seen Dr Jekyll, but you'll soon see Mr Hyde. Remember, you should never wrestle with a chimney sweep, unless absolutely necessary. She says that she is just like any lady you might meet anywhere, but to be honest she is a mad woman who ought never to have been allowed out of the Asylum."

She was right of course. I had met one version of Mabel, but for a while I went about with the idea that I had met a wonderful lady who must surely be doing Good in the world. My trouble is that I always seem to be able to see both sides of an argument, or even more. I want to think the best of people, so I'm easily robbed by tycoons and barrow-boys alike. I liked the IDEA of Mabel, just as I would believe any con-man who might try to sell me something. That way you often lose out by trusting people too much, but I suppose it's better than not trusting anyone at all. You have to be prepared to be fooled from time to time, because one day you might come face to face with something wonderful but don't dare believe it.

Mrs G went to the Community from time to time, but she told me I shouldn't visit again just yet. Instead, I got an idea of what their community life was like from meeting several visitors to the Community, who stayed with us in Mrs G's house for a few days. They were generally enthusiastic people who were polite but distant, as if living in a trance. It was as if when God had created them he changed his mind half-way through, and made something a bit different from the original plan. They were followers who were visiting to see Mabel's headquarters at first hand, and then make plans to move near her permanently. I remember some American gentlemen who came separately, and I thought how wonderful it was that Mabel could bring people from so far away. One of them was a bit of a dandy, with a top hat, and his skin looked orange rather than white. He stayed occasionally, until eventually he suddenly went away with a flea in his ear Mrs G said. There was some kind of rumour going about the Community that he was the man who started the war by writing to all the kings in Europe. I could never see how he could have done that, but apparently he did, and even boasted about it. He was a bit of a know-all, but we were never told exactly what he had done that was so wrong.

Another visitor who came quite a lot was Mrs Fox, a real lady. She travelled a long way, from Cornwall, and was one of those people who are never nasty to anyone. She wanted to live here but couldn't move till very nearly the time she died. She had known Mabel for a long time, but mainly from writing letters, and when she wasn't at Albany Road with the big-wigs she spent her time writing, writing, writing. She wrote books about Mabel, and when she came she always wanted people to tell her first-hand what had been happening since her last visit. I think she felt guilty that she didn't live in Bedford, and sometimes she seemed unhappy because Mabel had told her off about something or other. But I liked her, dotty though she was, and offered to post her letters as she was anxious that they get sent as quickly as possible to make sure they got to wherever they were going. She needn't have worried as the Castle Road post box had collections every day at 9, 11.15, 2.45, 5.15, 6.15, 7.15, and 8.45 and although it was only 6pm on Sundays, that didn't matter as she never sent things of a Sunday. Mrs G liked to talk with her, but if she criticised Mabel in any way, mentioning strange things she did, Mrs Fox refused to talk any more. "She thinks all Mabel's geese are swans" Mrs G would say.

It wasn't till I went to Albany Road one day in about 1924 that I really found out what they were like. Mrs G sent me to take some things to Number 12 and The Haven in a hurry, as they were having an important meeting later that day. I went to The Haven to find Amy the servant. I liked Amy, though I think she was a bit lazy. Once, when Mrs Firth asked her to do something, she just said "No. I've got a bone in my leg" which I thought was very cheeky. She could be a right botty mawther, she could. I knocked, but no one answered the door so I let myself in at the back of the house and said out loud "Hello. Is anyone there please?" I thought I heard a noise upstairs so I went up to the first floor, by the case of pinned dead butterflies on the landing, and politely asked again. It was important that they had the goods for the meeting I thought. I

96

knocked on a door or two and was about to go when a very angry man rushed out and pushed me down the stairs and out into the garden. He was red in the face and it frightened me as he shouted, hugely wild.

" How DARE you! You do NOT shout in the corridors. You do NOT knock on doors. You do NOT come in uninvited."

"B ..b... b...but it's important sir. I need to see my f...f...f...friend Amy."

" You WILL obey house rules. You WILL NOT talk in corridors.... And you must NOT have Amy as a friend."

He then blundered off, leaving me with Amy who had at last arrived.

"Don't worry about the Major. He's often like that, a stickler for the rules. I get that from most of them two or three times a week. You get used to it."

Amy told me about the House Instructions that members had to obey in Community houses. I hadn't known about these rules, as Mrs G hadn't told me about them, other than to say that guests in **her** house could do as they pleased as long as they didn't upset anyone else. In the proper Community houses they couldn't talk on the stairs, couldn't talk in the corridors, couldn't shout from one room to another. They HAD to keep their room tidy, they could have only one hot bath per week, they could only go to the Cinema or Theatre if Mrs Goodwin gave permission, and only twice a week at most. They must NOT have friendships outside the Community, they must never lend or borrow money, they must never give money to charities, and should sit without moving, feet together and hands on lap. They must be in bed, ready for lights out at 11.00. Mrs Barltrop insisted on decorum and good manners, and even told people off for not eating quietly or properly. She was very strict about Manners. It was almost like a prison.

I gave the things to Amy and went into the garden of Mabel's house to deliver the others. Hiding in a corner on a concrete seat was a young woman, behind some tall hollyhocks in flower, but strangely there were also some nettles, with dust on them. I like the dust on nettles. I guessed that the woman must be Mabel's daughter Dilys. She had obviously been crying, so I went and sat next to her, in silence. After a while I found something to say. "I hate seeing anyone being upset. If it's something that you can't do anything about, then its best to accept it, but if you can then have a good cry then think how you can sort things out." She put her arms round me for a moment.

"They are all horrible. I'm the only one available. He bumps into me in the garden all the time. He does it on purpose. He finds ways to touch my hand. He always watches me. They all do."

I didn't know what to say, but before I could say anything she got up. An aeroplane was passing over us in the clear sky, above the Garden of Eden, above God's granddaughter Dilys, and as the tone of the engines changed she looked up and stared at it. Quietly, with unblinking eyes, she said "There are people in that aeroplane, looking down at me in this garden. If only they knew about the Hell that they are flying over."

For a while after that day, I wanted to see Dilys to perhaps help her or at least do something to cheer her up, but we were hardly ever in the same place at the same time, try as I might to create a chance meeting. We did get to know each other better later on, when Evelyn was around, and when she was happy she was a good person to be with, but at that time she was lonely and seemed to have a blank mind. Once, when I bumped into her in town, she stared at me and said:

"How are...you.....how........have you been.........It's ..a long time ....since ......we ....last ....met."

I didn't know what to say so we said nothing more. We never spoke about that meeting in the garden again, but I think she must have appreciated me trying to be kind to her; and as much as it was possible for me to be a friend to her, I think I was just that.

As I got to see the members of the Community more and more, I realised how strange they were. Some were strange in a harmless way, others were strange in a way that meant you couldn't trust them. You certainly wouldn't want them to be your next door neighbour. In fact, over the years, me and Mrs G were lucky in the neighbours we had in Castle Road, only a few hundred yards from Albany Road, but half the world away in atmosphere. On one side from about 1930 we had the Clancy family, with the house passing from one generation to another, all of them as good a neighbour as you could hope for. The first ones were Tom and Janet, who had several children, but only Gary stayed there, eventually taking the house on himself after his parents died. On the other side there were several couples, but the only ones I remember much about were the Italians, Maria and Tony, who moved here in the early 1960's. They were some of the Italian immigrants who came to the town in the 1950's from a little town where there wasn't much work, so they came to Bedford to the nearby brickworks. Maria and Tony were very, very old fashioned in all they did, keeping their Italian traditions even though they were now miles from home. I felt ever so sorry for their clever daughter Carmela, a typical Italian girl with long black hair and big brown eyes, who always obeyed her father. She was due to marry an Italian boy, and big preparations were made, but just before the day her aunt died so as per tradition, the wedding had to be postponed as a mark of respect. She went into mourning and dressed all in black. When that time was over another date was fixed, but again, another relative died in Italy so there had to be another period of mourning. They did get married in the end. I went to Maria's funeral at the Italian church, and remember that it was packed. The priest said not a word of English. The whole Italian community came to pay their respects, but also to have a friendly get together with their countrymen. It brought a tear to my eye to think that they were all so kind to the other members of their community.

Oh yes, I remember another neighbour down the road as well. He had been in the second war, and whenever he saw anything that had been made in Germany, like a Volkswagen car, he would shout out a warning to the street: "Messerschmitt! Messerschmitt!" He was funny, and didn't mean anything nasty by that.

Mrs G and me got on well with all our neighbours. Much later on, the Clancys sort of made me one of the family and I helped Eve with her writing. She loved making stories up, you know. She was clever, but no-one knows how much she owes to me.

What else do I remember about the Panaceans? I'll have to think, but yes, there was a lot more skulduggery, especially to do with poor Mrs Firth …

A Fly. A Solitary Fly

History is written, so they say, by the victors. Churchill said that he knew History would look kindly on him – because he was going to physically write it, from his point of view. And he most certainly did. What we know about events in the Panacea Campus may therefore be flawed. So how about a bit of unbiased reporting …

This bit is from the viewpoint of a fly. Yes, a fly.

Now I know you'll think this a bit unlikely, that a common or garden housefly can bring something to the table so to speak, about the Panacea Society, but sometimes the unlikely is possible. After all, magicians can make things appear and disappear, politicians can convince people that Black is White, and so on. There's the theory that if you had an infinite number of chimps at an infinite number of typewriters for an infinite period of time, then eventually one would write the whole of Shakespeare's plays, word perfect. No one can ever test this one way or the other, but it's an interesting thought. So if that is possible, then it's just as possible that a fly might be able to observe things happening around it, and have fly-like thoughts about them. They have an advantage, as they have loads of eyes, pointing in all directions, so they don't miss much. And perhaps other animals can communicate, animals such as jackdaws and squirrels who were long term residents in the Garden of Eden.

So there you go then, let's play our part in the wish that most people have some time or another:

" I'd like to be a fly on the wall" and look at the events at 12 Albany Road in 1923.....what would the fly have seen?

He would have seen a man with orange-looking skin who these days tended to strut around the place like the prospective new owner of a house just waiting for the contracts to be exchanged and can hardly wait for the big day to arrive. He would have seen that man at night time, outside the bedroom of another man in a Community

house, waiting to go in.
!!!**

He would have seen hands on shoulders *****and *********and
**********. Then he saw ************ and ***
elsewhere************************************and   furtive
goings on which the fly didn't understand. *********************
************. He would have seen the man talking to others,******
making himself out to be a powerful force who had started the war.
He would have seen the woman who was in charge looking about in
all directions, asking things of her companions, nervous of being near
the orange man.********************.
On another occasion, he would have seen a smaller, older man
standing between the two others while loud words were being said
******_____ ****_____. The small, wizened man was firm
and would not let the other man near the woman, protecting her.
He would have seen another, older woman sitting with the first woman
and the small wizened man in a room together. The second woman
suddenly went into a trance with her hands on her lap and spoke in a
different voice. "Send the man to New York. He will die."

The fly at this point decided to buzz about at the window, irritating the
women. The small man went to the window and instead of swatting
it dead, opened the window and kindly said " go you poor devil, get
thee gone. Why should I hurt thee? This world is surely wide enough
to hold both thee and me." But the fly decided to stay put and watch
the rest of the performance.

*(An American, Edgar Peissart, came to Bedford in 1922 and quickly
became one of 'The Four,' Mabel's inner group of supporters, but very
soon had hopes of taking over from her. Kate Firth was wary, saying that
he looked like the Devil, and soon Mabel was worried that he might try
to take over. He was gathering support from previously loyal women like
Helen Morris, and via his taking advantage of the latent homosexuality
of some males in the community, especially Donald Ricketts.*

Peter Rasmussen was of course completely loyal to her and at one point there was almost a punch up between them. Emily Goodwin solved the problem by suddenly discovering that she was, in fact, the 'Instrument of the Divine Mother.' She would go into a trance and speak messages from The Divine Mother, Mabel's Holy Mother and the fourth part of the "Foursquare God." From then on, the Divine Mother would speak via Goodwin and direct Mabel in what she should do. In early 1923, she said that Peissart would die in New York, and encouraged Mabel to set about getting rid of him. He was to go on trial).

A while later, the fly would have seen the Divine Mother and her Daughter with yet another man who was frightened. He admitted his sins. The older woman had a knife, the man was on his knees, thinking he was to be sacrificed. The woman shook him, shouted at him, stared wide eyed at the ceiling, shook uncontrollably, said prayers, and finally shook the Devil from his body. " I the DIVINE MOTHER JERUSALEM command this devil to get out!" The man curled himself up into a ball, frightened to look, frightened to move. All he could do was cry.

The older woman calmed down and stood still, watching and listening. The fly buzzed over and landed on the man's head, but he was too frightened to swish it away. The leader, Mabel, looked kindly on the man and gave him some milk and food.

(Later, they carried out the Trial of Edgar Peissart, the orange skinned man, but in reality it was Satan that they were putting on trial. Although homosexual practices were a sin and illegal, what they were more concerned about was that it symbolised a rejection of Women and Mabel's leadership).

Later still, the fly would have seen the orange man being taken, subdued and psychologically beaten, to an address in Castle Road where his possessions had been secretly moved from his Community room. It would have told other flies that the man never came back again, and the two women and the small wizened man prayed together in relief and joy.

(Peissart did, in fact, go to New York and very soon afterwards he died, thus fulfilling Goodwin's, well, the Divine Mother's, prophecy. After that Goodwin heard voices more and more, regularly going into a trance and speaking in tongues. The goings on in the Community became more and more unhinged and in Goodwin's case, raving. The members of an increasingly important organisation with influence over thousands of people were now being led by two unstable women instead of one.

But if the fly thought the events of early 1923 were extreme, his descendants would see even more eccentricities and delusions).

Etholle
Witchfinders

I have to say that the next few years after meeting Mabel in 1921 were the strangest of my life, not Strange Ha-Ha, or even Strange Peculiar, but often Strange Frightening. For a time, until I got back to being calm and normal again after the incident at The Haven, I was scared and helpless to know what to think, but Mrs G was always there to understand. I know now what was happening, but at the time everything seemed like a madhouse, which it was really I suppose. I heard things from Amy, Mrs Fox, Mrs G and from overhearing conversations between Mrs Bull and Mrs G that I shouldn't have heard.

It turned out that Emily Goodwin, a fairly anonymous member who just happened to live at Mabel's house to look after aunt Fanny, gradually became someone Mabel completely relied upon. Mabel had got worried because the American Edgar Peissart (him with the orange skin) was trying to take over from her. There were also rumours of some kind of hanky-panky going on between him and other men – but those who knew the details didn't say exactly what it was and I'm glad about that because it sounds horrid. Anyway, one day Mrs Goodwin suddenly put her hands on her lap, closed her eyes and then started speaking in a different voice. Apparently she said she was speaking the words given to her by the Divine Mother, who they all thought was part of God. She was the Instrument of the Divine Mother, so she was sort of talking to Mabel who was her daughter! She told Mabel to get rid of Mr Peissart, who would die soon after. That's exactly what they did somehow and I remember that one evening all his things were brought here; he then arrived later on, looking like death warmed up he was, and he went away the next morning.

Mabel was really ill at that time, really nervy, really suffering from all sorts of things, and Mrs Goodwin took over in a way. I don't think Mabel was really aware when her aunt Fanny died and she definitely didn't go to the funeral. They did plan it so that she was buried next to Ellen Oliver, though, with a nice inscription on the stone. Mabel was in charge, but a lot of what she did was only after being told by Mrs Goodwin. She kept on having these messages about what Mabel should do next but she never tried to take over officially. A lot of what Mabel was doing was good, especially the Healing Mission that became very popular all over the country, and they kept on producing all the leaflets about opening the box that they said was so important. On the other hand, things they did got stranger and stranger.

Mrs Goodwin said that there were lots of Evil forces in the world, not just Satan, Beelzebub, Lucifer and the rest, but even prehistoric monsters that lived on in a spirit way, many of them in the Garden Room, the Chapel itself! Mrs Goodwin had to fight them to beat them and kill them. The first one was a bear, then a giant sloth that made people depressed. It stunk to high heavens as well she said. She used a stick from an olive tree to help her, and some of the battles lasted for hours. One was a dragon, that had taken over a man, and she roared at it and forced it into the corner of the room "I command you to let this man go free. Leave the man!" She drew a line on the ground so it couldn't move away and then killed it and cut it into pieces. Another beast had huge tusks and nostrils. Another was a cloud of fiery snakes that attacked her in her chair before she could even start. She normally drove the monster into the South-East corner of the room and in fact a palm tree there gradually died as well. She would stab and hack at the monsters, huge though they were. Mrs Goodwin would fight for ages, stabbing at the air, the ground and all around her as the monsters tried to beat her. Once she had nearly beaten one when Mabel called out that there was another one creeping up on her from behind. She stopped, exhausted, had a drink of the Holy Water, then with new strength beat them both. When she had won she would pant, out of breath, and then stand with a foot on the body and arms folded looking exactly like the woman on the War Memorial statue not far away. Another was a giant seven feet tall, with red hair, another was a gorilla, another was Goliath, but she beat them all, and cut off Goliath's head. Afterwards, she told Peter to bury the palm tree, but she had no memory at all of the battles she had fought, just sitting there covered in sweat.

Once, when she recovered from a fight, panting with exhaustion and her long hair all tangled up and clothes dishevelled, she said in astonishment

" Whatever have I been doing?"

Mrs Fox told us most of this and I was frightened to think that our world had such things in it and I hadn't even noticed. It got even scarier when they decided to expel evil spirits that were lurking in the Community houses, casting them out either by going through ceremonies in the Garden Room, with an empty chair in the middle, or by going to the house itself. They sent instructions that each member must send details of any relation who suffered from any mental or nervous affliction, any moral failings, any ugly habits or any abnormality at all, as these were things to be cast out. Mrs G joked that the list was likely to be pretty long. They cast out the evil from all Religious orders, from the countries of the Empire, from the Legal profession and the Universities. They even decided to cast out Death itself. "My goodness, they've got their work cut out" said Mrs G.

The most frightening time was when Mrs Goodwin came to our house to cast out the evil spirits here, not that we knew there were any; it always seemed a quiet pleasant home to my mind. I'd only met Mrs Goodwin once before, when we passed in the garden. She just stopped dead and said "Who are you, girl?" Mabel didn't come of course, as it was more than 77 steps from her house. Mrs Goodwin came with Mrs Fox and the Green sisters, looking very stern and determined. She went into every room, from cellar to attic, spouting words from the Psalms, and had terrible fights with spirits in several rooms and won them all. They would suddenly attack her on the stairs or from behind a door and she would shriek and shout at them. She ran up and down the stairs three steps at a time, never falling over, and chased them into corners, normally driving them to the North or the East, driving away the invisible devils. Then all was quiet, with her panting and sweating, and suddenly coming out of her trance. I gave her a glass of water, not the Holy Water, and it was like a spider feeling a tug on it's web. She grabbed my hand, not letting it go, holding me fast:

*"This is **not** the Water, girl. **Andrews** girl. **Luggy** Andrews girl."*

Her eyes were still, cold, the look of someone herself possessed by a devil, yet she was now back to her normal self. After a few seconds she let me go, put the glass down still full, and left without any more words, but as she closed the door I think I heard a madcap laugh. I felt as if something was crawling down my throat and hacking away at my stomach, trying to get out.

How could she have known my nickname from school? Perhaps she really did have powers.

I cried and cried and no one could stop me. I knelt and prayed and had no sleep that night.

From then on, I stayed like a wallflower at a party (not that I'd been to many) and going to Albany Road as little as possible. I didn't know how such a woman as Mabel could let Mrs Goodwin act as she did, but I thought that it must be because there had been devils to cast out. Mrs G said this was normal for what went on at the Community, and that having carried out the casting she wouldn't come here again. She herself seemed to have been scared as well, but could hide it better than I could. She said it was best to keep quiet and try to change things secretly, that she was a catalyst, working in the shadows; she was a 'shadowy catalyst' which I thought was a strange way to describe herself. Unfortunately, just afterwards, Mrs G had a stroke and hardly ever left the house until she died in 1935. Perhaps she was scared into a stroke, if that's possible. But I'm getting ahead of myself....

Mrs Fox kept us informed about what was happening when she made her frequent stays with us, but never said anything critical of Mabel or Mrs Goodwin. Once, she came back all excited about finding something important at Mabel's house. When Ellen Oliver was on her death-bed in 1921, Mabel decided she would be Mabel's messenger to God. Ellen had to recite the names of all 144 sealed members at that time, and had the written prayers of all the followers on a silver bowl at her side so she could present them to God. No one thought she would die, but if it had to happen, then they would find significance in it. In fact, said Mrs Fox, several members had seen angels and cherubs in the sky around the house the day she died, so that meant God was aware of her importance. That was surprising really, as she had died in a house in Adelaide Square, on the other side of the town, in a bedroom facing Bedford Prison of all things, so why had the angels flown around Albany Road? Anyway, Mrs Fox said that she and Mabel had found the prayers and the list of names while they were rummaging in a drawer at 12 Albany Road, purely by chance, as they had been shoved in there and forgotten. She was delighted about it, but I thought that if it had been so important, why hadn't Mabel kept it safe, or even had it buried in the coffin? This was in 1926 - so much for respect for the Dead, or even for the Messenger to God! Mrs G slurred that she wasn't surprised. She could make her sarcastic comments right till the end, which I was pleased about.

Mrs G had never believed in the Healing, and didn't use the linen and water. But as I was so worried about her, I did use it for her for a few weeks without her knowing that I'd put it in her tea and for washing her face. It made no difference at all though. Actually, I must admit that I did try it myself a few times, for colds and so on, in secret, so only me and God would know. It didn't work for me either, but even if it had, I think I would have kept quiet as it seemed a rather embarrassing naughty secret to have.

At the same time as that visit from Mrs Fox, I saw Joe the bus driver selling poppies from his bus, the first year after the factory had started. It was a wonderful idea to try and help old soldiers like Harry (who was still about) and Albert (who had never come back) but after I'd given him some money one of the Community men tore the poppy off me saying that I must NOT give money to any charity. It was a rule. He also said someone like Joe couldn't possibly do any Good in the world as he didn't have a soul and I should never talk to people like him unless giving them orders. I think he was horrible to Joe. That scared me as well and I think I must have been a very quiet nervous person at that time.

I prayed a lot then, and called Mabel Octavia as I thought it for the best. Once I was in Octavia's house and she started shouting that she saw the face of an ugly aboriginal in the folds of her coat, she saw cloven hoofs under a chair and the horns of the Devil. She wasn't that lovely lady I had once met, but a nervous woman that I pitied, and the only help she got was from people who went along with the things that she had made up and made it worse and worse. When I came home Mrs G would calm me down in her way, but it wasn't easy.

One good thing was that there was a friendly young lady who joined at that time. I was sitting at the roundabout in Rothsay Road and I saw two ladies (real ladies, not women) going in and out of number 19 – the house I had always liked. Muriel was the older sister, who bossed Evelyn about. They were rich, but Evelyn liked nothing more than to muck about mending her car or pottering in the garden, a bit of a tomboy I suppose. Evelyn must have been 27 at the time so she and Dilys were the youngest there. Evelyn was fun to be with when she felt like it, though she would suddenly remember her higher station in life and cut me off which made me sad as I never had much chance to be with younger people.

The worst trouble was about Mrs Firth, and I got to hear about it from her servant Amy. Mrs Firth had always been Mabel's good friend, despite being a bit jealous perhaps. But she started to think that things were getting rather silly when Mrs Goodwin became the Instrument of the Divine Mother. Actually several people thought that was a load of nonsense, and some people left the Society because of it. Mrs Fox wrote that some told her "When Octavia did it all, it was very nice, very nice indeed," but nothing would make them believe Mrs Goodwin was the Instrument of the Divine Mother. Mrs Firth had given The Haven to be the main building for the Society activities, with people staying there for meetings and events. She got friendly with a new member, Mr Tucker – who funnily enough, also had orange looking skin. He was something of a clairvoyant. He believed in Octavia, but he refused to believe anything Mrs Goodwin said. He thought her a fraud and a charlatan. She claimed to know things by working in mysterious ways but he said she only knew things because she got others to act as spies and tell her about every little thing that was going on. She wanted all the rumours and title-tattle. One day, Amy showed me a pack of notes that Mrs Goodwin had accidentally left on a table in The Haven. It was some slips written by many people in the Community saying things like: "I saw Mrs F with Mr T in town today. He raised his hat to me" or "Mr T walked with Mrs F by the Embankment this morning. She was dressed too young for her age. They nodded to me" or "I saw Mr T at Braggins today. He did not raise his hat. He was on the other side of the road." They were for Mrs Goodwin.

Amy said that they had all been finding evidence of wrong-doing by Mrs Firth and Mr Tucker. He kept telling her go to a doctor about her bad eye, but Mrs Goodwin kept saying she must not, as the Holy Water would cure it. In the end, there was a terrible hoo-ha at a meeting when Mrs Firth told everyone that the whole thing especially the "Divine Mother" was a nonsense and a failure, and she was leaving. Mabel was in tears, a broken woman, and Amy had seen it all. Mabel tried to speak to Mrs Firth afterwards but it made no difference. Mr Tucker told them Mrs Goodwin had no powers at all, and the things she knew were only because of her spies. Mrs Firth said that her house was no longer to be used by the Society, and they must move all their things out. Also, the access to the garden of the Haven from the Garden Room of Mabel's house must be bricked up. It was a terrible scene, chaos and panic and crying. Mabel wandered about as white as a sheet and could hardly speak.

Later, Mr Tucker told Amy that Mrs Goodwin must be possessed by an evil entity and if she really was the Divine Mother then she would have been able to use her power to beat Mrs Firth. Later again, he told her that the whole Visitation malarkey was a right scream, and it was preposterous to think that God would choose such a set of old people, cripples and the feeble-minded to do his work. He made fun of everything dear to Mabel and her followers.

I only heard about this from Amy and Mrs G wasn't in with them all at that time, so perhaps I never got the full story, but I know that

Mrs Firth moved away with Mr Tucker and I think they had a happy married life. She sold The Haven a few months later, and it was Mabel who bought it! I don't know for sure, but apparently Mrs Firth knew this was on the cards and let it happen. All the things were moved back into The Haven, and Peter knocked down the wall into the Haven again, with great rejoicing and ceremony. I did hear that they kept in touch with Mrs Firth, hoping she would come back. But she never did. Mrs G had a lot of time for Mrs Firth, and was unhappy that she had left like that and I think it meant Mabel relied more and more on Mrs Goodwin and Peter to protect her. Actually, Mrs Firth reminded me of Mrs G a lot, so perhaps that's why I quite liked her compared with the others.

Dilys was badly effected by all this, and I sometimes saw her walking about in the streets looking blankly around. I did try to speak to her but she didn't seem to recognise me. A few more of the followers left about that time, but the ones left were more and more sure of their faith in Mabel and Mrs Goodwin. In fact afterwards the membership grew and grew, because of all the publicity about the Healing and the Box. They were headline news. They were like a gang, getting security for themselves from being a closed group. But they could also be like a pack of cruel animals.

Then when they bought the school building in 1930 they were able to open up all the gardens to make the big campus that Mabel was so proud of and meant they could stroll around in the Garden of Eden. Everything was going well on the face of it, but poor Dilys was getting worse, moving around from one house to another, hardly ever feeling at home and always wary of the people near her. Poor cow.

I jumped from periods of sheer terror to being religious to being content in my own little world looking after Mrs G. I was worried about the future as I had no idea what would happen to me when Mrs G died, as she surely would soon. In the end, Mrs G managed to make some kind of will so that when she died I would live in her house for as long as I wanted, probably till I myself died, but it must still be a property that could be used by the Society. She made no instruction on what should happen when I died, but as that was years away I wasn't worried about it. I did think it strange that she said I wouldn't ever get a Pension, like some other people had when they got old, but I also had the income from her investments so I had no money worries at all. In some ways I was a lady of substance and I could choose how I could live.

When you are young, you don't think too much about the future, do you?

Happy Families 1933

"The customer is always right. The customer is always right. The customer is always right" repeated Ted Simmons. "The customer is always right. Even if she is wrong. And a looney."

He knocked at the door of 12 Albany Road, and waited some time until a small woman opened it just a fraction, realised who it was, and sharply spat out "We don't want any trouble. Go to the side gate. You can go and see for yourself. Be quick, and then go."

He heard the noise of the gate being unlocked, and as he opened it, saw the woman dart back into the door at the side of the house. The door was closed. Firmly.

He strolled to the back of the property, with the walk of a well-fed gardener. The long building there had been partly finished by his building firm, and was now, apparently, a chapel. He had had complaints about his workmanship, unjustifiably he thought, for unlike this customer he actually knew what he was doing. He had added a few improvements to what they had wanted, making the overall design better but they had complained. 'Frequent mistakes of the workmen following out their own ideas of how the scheme should be carried out' the letter said. Well, he'd take a quick look to work out what he'd need to modify the work (he preferred to use the word uglify rather than modify) then get it done the next day. They were good payers – reliable – but sometimes difficult. There's an awkward sod in most streets of most towns, though it had to be said that Albany Road had more than its fair share of them.

"Shoddy workmanship. My eye!" He muttered.

Having sized up what was needed – just a few small changes – he looked around at the garden. Secluded, quiet and luxurious, it made him wish he could have it himself. Ah, but there was the owner, Mrs Barltrop, on the other side of the lawn. He had rarely seen her during the work, as they were given clear instructions on their limited access to the site. Go in, do the work, get out. She had always seemed distant, as if there was something going on in her mind that he couldn't fathom, but all of a sudden she would snap to attention, and say exactly what she wanted. Very precise and clearly thought out. Even if his ideas had been better.

She was some kind of mad woman – they all were – but her money was good. Loads of women, living together. Definitely a bit queer. Mostly ugly old bats, though a few younger ones. The blokes were no danger to the women, he thought. That little one, Peter, had balls though. He'd managed to make a small window in the wall to the attic, really high up it was. Only used a ladder. That was quite brave of him – must have been determined to get it done. Always scurrying around doing things, following that Mrs Barltrop around like a little puppy. Seemed a decent chap though. Mrs Goodwin was a different case, and he was glad she wasn't around. She had two personalities, and he wasn't sure which was worse. A very hard taskmaster.

They reckoned Mrs Barltrop was a religious nut. A prophet, here in Bedford. She could cure people who were ill. All over the world. Well, she often looked a bit peaky herself, so she couldn't be much good at it could she? They all treated her with such respect and awe. It must be strange to be in the same house as such an important person, getting daily messages from God. Apparently. Still, everyone to their own. If it didn't harm him, he thought, then it was alright. You could make allowances for good payers.

Across the lawn, in the sunshine, the Daughter of God played with her son's daughter, Anna. The two year old ran to Mabel, shouting with happiness as they played. Mabel threw a ball, Anna tried to catch it but missed. They both laughed. Anna threw the ball to Mabel, who leant forward to catch but it was too far away. Laughing, Anna ran and handed it to Mabel, who sat down, tired and out of breath, on a stone bench. Anna put her little arms around her grandmother and pushed her chubby fingers into Mabel's mouth as they both laughed. From across the lawn, Dilys came towards them, playfully pretending to hide behind bushes as she got nearer. Anna saw her and ran with arms waving in the air, giggling as she went. Dilys pretended to fall over, rolled onto her back and Anna, with a smile, sat down on her aunt's belly. She lay flat and pushed her little fingers into Dilys's mouth as they both laughed, just as she had with Mabel. Dilys put her arms around the warm body of her niece and they cuddled each other, laying on the grass, in the sunshine, in the Garden of Eden.

Mabel, Dilys and Anna, all smiling and happy. A Perfect Moment. Something to take the sting out of the rest of the day.

Ted looked away, embarrassed, and quietly walked towards the gate, unseen. Sometimes that Mrs Barltrop seemed pretty well normal.

Ceremonials

—————>◆<—————

Some members of religious groups thrive on ceremonies and regalia. Panacea Society members were no exception. Quite apart from the detailed instructions on manners, etiquette and everyday life in the Community, the Society developed complicated and frankly baffling terminology for much of what they did.

Miss Hodgkinson was "Superintendant of the Commissariat"
Peter Rasmussen was "The Friend of the Bridegroom," amongst other titles
Ellen Oliver was the Eighth Angel of the Book of Revelation
Emily Goodwin was The Instrument of The Divine Mother
The Doctrine of the Anchor within the Veil
The Order of The Ten
The Forty Five
The Apostles
Director of Protection Work
The Sixty six
The Four
The Burning of the Faggots
Dead Sea People
Wilderness People
Sealed
White Seal
Red Seal
Crimson Seal

Royal Seal

Blah blah blah

The best example of this is the terminology for the process of Sealing, with all the various stages:

PHASE 1
Your name is written in the Book of the Multitude
You then passed through the Preliminary Acts of
1 The Marriage Vow
2 The Oath of Allegiance
3 The Confession
4 Homage to the King
5 Homage to the Queen
6 The Casting of Controls
7 The Cleansing of the Body
8 The Treatment of Ailments and the Command to the Solar Plexus
9 The Sprinkling

PHASE 2- The Destruction of the Mortal Soul
1 You were met at the lych Gate
2 You passed under the Sword
3 You handed in your Declaration
4 You received two glasses of water
The Divine Mother, as you drank the water, counting the 12 strokes like those of a funeral bell, signifying the death of the mortal Soul

PHASE 3 – The Withering of the Mortal Mind
1 The Opening of the Door by the Divine Mother, that the black birds might fly forth
2 The cleansing of the infested area by the Sprinkling of the Blessed Water on the head

PHASE 4- The Cursing of the Fig Tree

These four phases made up the process of The Sealing, though what it looked like in practice is anybody's guess – there is definitely a love of Ceremony and Regalia. The terms used are meant to impress and probably strike fear in the member at various points, Peter Rasmussen had to wave a sword about and pierce pieces of paper. Well, he does seem to have liked a bit of dressing up ….

The above list is for Lionel Carew-Hunt, and the original was kept by him until his death, as it was so important to him. When he died in 1972 aged 92, he was blind and deaf, but still lived in a sub-standard property in Albany Road, where he had extensive burns from scalding hot water, yet the next day his cause of death was given as 'Heart Failure.'

The words used by The Instrument of The Divine Mother in particular are pretty well incomprehensible, amounting to gibberish on occasion.

"You have come over from the Help which was on the left-hand side, to the Power to overcome on the right hand side, and now you have passed under the Rod and the Sceptre, you will have the power to overcome" was a ceremonial comment made which would have made sense to the member, but not to us nowadays, I suspect.

But it sounds impressive, like this mumbo-jumbo from 'The Life Of Brian.'

"There shall in that time be rumours of things going astray and there shall be great confusion as to where things really are and nobody will really know where lieth those little things with the sort of raffiawork base that has an attachment. At that time a friend shall lose his friend's hammer and the young shall not know where lieth the things possessed by their fathers that their fathers put there the night before about eight o'clock."

Or, again, like something from "Alice in Wonderland,"where the Mock Turtle's school teaches versions of subjects that aren't quite as they should be:

Reeling and Writhing, Arithmetic (Ambition, Distraction, Uglification and Derision), Mystery (Ancient and Modern), Seaography, Drawling (including Stretching and Fainting in Coils) and Classics (Laughing and Grief).

Yes, the Ceremonies and the Terminologies used are from a different, imagined world.

16th October 1934

Everything in the room was still. No noise. Quiet as the grave, well, almost. The whole house was going through the motions of being busy as usual, but some downstairs had edginess in all they did. Whispered conversations in corners. Worried looks. Frowns. Suppressed tears. A handkerchief, quickly taken out to blow a nose that didn't need to be blown or wiped, then slowly put back into the sleeve of a cardigan, worn daily in this place dedicated to the work of the one upstairs who was their whole world, but not long for it. Only a few knew the truth of what was happening. In the Sitting Room two figures sat or occasionally paced about, sometimes going to a Bible on the table, flicked through the pages hopefully, anxiously, looked up as if about to pronounce some wisdom, then sat down again, crestfallen and beaten. Silence again.

Upstairs, the small bedroom for the servant was empty. So was the large room at the front, Mrs Goodwin's room, though it always seemed that someone was there. You always felt that she was watching; she was everywhere. At the back of the house, Dilys lay on her bed, staring at the ceiling, door shut. The upper room, where once the devotions had been carried out was empty, but open for the despondent to sit, sharing it with Angst instead of the Hwyl of happier times. In the attic, Peter stared out of the small window, looking to the South, distraught, as he was one who knew what was happening in the room below.

In Mabel's bedroom nothing moved, but from the mantelpiece Dilys' eyes looked out at her mother's final domain. This was the centre of the world, the Royal Domain, Eden. The whole universe was here. But now, God's daughter was laying motionless in a bed, in a small room, in a small town, dying. The dying person's world is small, limited, one of frustration and contempt.

Mabel Barltrop, God's Daughter, was dead.

IN LOVING MEMORY OF

M.B.

OCT 16 1934

"I AM THE RESURRECTION AND THE LIFE"

O. S-J.

"IN MOUNT ZION AND IN JERUSALEM SHALL BE
DELIVERANCE"

"O - She has gone....my only hope."

(Diary of Peter Rasmussen, October 1934).

Etholle
Old Crones

There was lots happening in the next few years, but I tried to keep away from all the uproars and arguments. Mrs G sometimes wanted me to take her to the services and we both sat there like fish out of water, especially as she couldn't speak properly, but we tried to seem good. Mrs Barltrop didn't seem to recognise us, and Mrs Goodwin ignored us as we weren't proper members. We did go to the Garden Parties which were lovely and even Mrs Barltrop was a different person when she was with all the members from across the country, and who she only saw from time to time. She wrote the words for a play about Alice in Wonderland one year and she looked like a little girl, clapping her hands and jumping out of her seat. Everyone had fun, even Miss Dilys.

Miss Dilys was definitely very ill with worry or panics or something, and you didn't know what kind of mood she'd be in from one day to the next. They moved her from one house to another so she never settled. She liked it at Evelyn Gillett's house, and at The Haven sometimes, but when she moved on she seemed lost and she would snap at people. Even when she lived nearby, she didn't try to come and see me, and if we bumped into each other she might be very pleased to see me and say we should go out soon, but she never called. I waited and waited and waited. In the end Evelyn had to take her to stay a while with the Community in France somewhere as she was so bad but when she came back she still wasn't right.

I tried to keep Mrs G up to date with what I knew, and she had a lot of visits from Mrs Bull and Rita who knew more than me. At one time, Miss Dilys had gone to stay with Rita and was so ill that Rita told Mrs Bull something had to be done, because she was so depressed she wanted to die. Mrs G said if Dilys could leave the "mess of mad old crones who plot and pray and get menopausal together" (well, I think that's what she said) she might be normal again. Mrs Bull got really worked up, determined to save her niece. She went to the Gillett house shouting, then to see Mrs Peck, who was normally a sensible person compared with the others. Then to The Haven where Miss Dilys was in a normal mood playing the piano. Mrs Bull said Miss Dilys didn't want to come with her (probably because she was too scared) so she came back to see Mrs G. A bit later she went to see the Gilletts again and argued with Muriel at the gate for ages. She didn't give up till nearly ten o'clock when it was getting dark. Adrian Barltrop also came at that time and tried to tell his mother how ill Miss Dilys was, but nothing much happened and she stayed there getting worse and worse. Poor Mrs Bull and Rita never gave up, but they couldn't speak to her, and their letters probably were stopped by Mrs Goodwin or one of the Green sisters. Mrs G gave up as well, but told me I should always try to help Miss Dilys if I should ever see her, or just cheer her up if I could.

When Mrs Barltrop died no one knew for days afterwards and it was only when Mrs Bull heard about it that things were arranged. Mrs G would have wanted to go to the funeral but she couldn't move well. They didn't even put a notice in the paper to let people know. Mrs Bull and Rita went to the funeral, though they weren't welcomed by the handful of members who went. I don't think Miss Dilys was there, or Mrs Goodwin, or Mr Rasmussen. Canon Payne did the service. She was buried in unconsecrated ground.

Mrs G sent some flowers from Laxtons and she cried that night.

After Mrs Barltrop died Mrs Fox still came to stay until in the end she bought a house and lived in Rothsay Gardens full time, so I got to hear things still. Mrs Fox still wrote a lot, though I don't think she was as important as when Mrs Barltrop was alive. As far as I could make out, Mrs Goodwin took over completely as the Council of the Society was to deal only with spiritual things but she would have full control over finances and the running of the place. Later, Mrs Fox had to resign as President and so Mrs Goodwin ran the whole thing. She was stern, and told Evelyn off in public if she was being immature (which she often was). I think she also took over poor Dilys' finances and didn't let her have any money, so she couldn't escape even if she was brave enough. Mr Rasmussen apparently was very well respected still but didn't want to get involved with things, just to carry on in his own way. I think he was heartbroken.

Although the Society carried on, I got more interested in what was going on in the town. It was the time I started going to Country Dancing meetings - *lovely fun*. I went to church properly, to St Paul's normally, not the services in the chapel. I met some very nice friendly people there who helped me sort things out after Mrs G died.

One big thing was when I heard about a march that was to go through the town. People were talking about a place called Jarrow somewhere a long way away, where there was high unemployment, so lots of people from there were marching all the way to London to try and get the government to help. I read about it in the paper when I was looking to see what was on at the pictures. ' Mr Deedes goes to Town' was on at the Granada starring Gary Cooper and I had to smile because on the other side of the page was an advertisement that said:

"Why does Mr Deedes come to Town?
Presumably because he wishes to shop in Bedford,
realising as others do, that
no town offers a higher standard
of Goods and Services.

He is sure to visit
BACCUS'S 35 High Street."

I thought there must be a very clever person working for Mr Baccus
the ironmonger, perhaps the same person who had put the giant metal
plough on the top of the building. They said that it had won prizes at
the Great Exhibition in 1851. If it hadn't then it should have done.
Anyway, the paper said that the men would be put up at the old library
in Harpur Street, the town would be giving them blankets, the Rotary
Club would provide tobacco, and they would have sausages given
by the Bedford Master Butchers' Association. Also, about 150 blind
marchers were coming from Manchester.

It all sounded exciting so I went to see them go at half past nine on
the Wednesday morning. They went from the Institute along Harpur
Street, Dame Alice and then the High Street to Luton. Everyone gave
them THREE CHEERS! and wished them well. I didn't know it but
they told me Bedfordshire had the lowest unemployment in the country
and Jarrow had one of the highest. Before they went there were speeches
from the MP for Jarrow who had a bad cold but still spoke for half an
hour and walked at the head of the march. I thought she was a wonderful
person and a good leader, like Mrs Barltrop had been once upon a time.
A few of the men were too ill to walk so a Removal firm drove them
instead and the Salvation Army helped as well.

The next week I read in the paper that Mr Neate, the mayor, had
said "one often finds that those whom we thought were friends were
not friends. The longer I live, the more clearly I see things and the
less dogmatic I become in my vision on politics, religion and affairs
in general." The paper said the Rev Colthurst had said "It is a tragedy
that there should be in some people's minds that the church should
be on the side of the Haves, and leave the Have Nots to fend for
themselves." I thought that was very true and I said so to Evelyn when
I happened to see her. She thought for a moment then said that Mrs
Barltrop had told all members to vote Conservative in an election, and
she disapproved of the Socialists. She had written down: "Each rank

in Society follows certain rules in addressing persons above it. There is no room for any kind of familiarity or Socialism in THIS Society." She said Socialism and Communism were the work of Satan. Most of the members were very well to do, thank you very much, so I suppose it was natural for them to not like the socialists, but it was good to hear the vicar standing up for them.

Not long after, I read about the nice Vicar of Stiffkey, Mr Davidson, who had been treated so unfairly a few years before when I lived by the sea. He had fallen on hard times, worse than before, and the paper said he had been eaten by by a lion called Freddie. This was in Skegness, with several vicars watching.

I didn't have much to do with the Panaceans again till about 1960 though I might bump into Evelyn or Miss Dilys or another one, Miss Hughes, a nervous woman who told me about the events. I did go back in the end though.

Etholle
Thinking About Things I Don't Understand

I got some false teeth today! They are uncomfortable and move about a lot. It's like they are trying to escape.

I think I must have been a bit of a recluse after Mrs G died in 1935. It was sad the way she lived on after having the stroke, and I think it might have been better if she'd died straight away. In the last weeks, all she could do was to lie in bed, able to move her head and one arm. At first, I tried to make her get up every day. I told her she had to sort of creep up on herself, to take herself by surprise and just get up. But she couldn't. She could still make her funny comments, but in the end she got worse. She couldn't speak or write, and her only word was something that sounded like "pain" but it didn't mean pain, as she said it when she was happy about something. I told her things that were going on and I knew from her face what she thought about it all. I could tell she was glad but embarrassed that I did everything for her, and although I think that in a way she was content she was also very frustrated. She was like that for the last year or so. Some of the Panaceans sorted things out when she died, and told me that they were forced to let me stay in the house although they weren't at all happy about it. They would be back in touch, but they never did mention it again. They found Mrs G's birth certificate in the house, and I saw that she had been born in Aberystwyth. Her mother's maiden name was Myfanwy Montez, and her father's name was Herod Jenkins. It was an unusual mixture of names, and I thought they must have had such interesting lives that one day someone ought to write a book about them.

I didn't leave the house much though if I bumped into someone like Evelyn we would have a little chat as if we were good friends who saw each other daily. Even though we didn't.

I sat at her roundabout quite a lot, hoping to see her "Dirty Overalls

Smile" that made me happy to be alive.

Perhaps I was a bit frightened because of the war, and I remember being scared when they put up a Poison Gas Detector at the junction of Castle Road and Albany Road, at the allotments. The Army took over some of the buildings and they wanted to have Castleside but had 8 Rothsay Gardens instead, as it was a very big place. They even took away a lot of the metal railings outside the houses.

I wanted to go to Mrs Fox's funeral out of respect, and waited for someone to tell me the details. No one told me. In the end I found out that she had been buried in Cornwall. Mrs Goodwin died as well. Actually a lot of them died at that time. A bit later, I went to the cemetery quite often with Mr Coghill. He was a nice Scottish gentleman who knew I wanted to put flowers on Mrs G's grave, and he pointed out where various members were buried. Mrs Goodwin had a headstone just like Mrs Barltrop's (though not so good quality) and Mr Coghill said this was all sorted out by Mr Rasmussen and Hilda Green. The words on the graves seemed a bit strange to me but he said it all made sense. Alice Jones, Canon Payne and Kate Hodgkinson all died at that time – all the important ones were going.

Before she died, Mrs Fox told me the answers to questions about my past. She was a nice lady, and I think she wanted to have a clear conscience before she died. She said that near the end of the Great War, my final guardian in Norfolk had been corresponding with other ladies such as Mrs Fox and Mabel about Joanna Southcott and her box. She was sure Mabel was a prophet and thought that I should go to live with Mr and Mrs G in Bedford. After all, something had to be done with me. I was known as Etholle Andrews, so that must be a divine indication I should follow Mabel, as her surname had also been Andrews. She even imagined that I might be related to Mabel. The guardian was a distant relation of Mr G, so she got in touch with Mrs G to suggest I live with her rather than write direct to Mabel as it might produce some embarrassment to her if we were related somehow. Mrs G would then introduce me to Mabel, who would surely recognise me by some divine way as being special, and I would join the Community.

However, by the time I came to Bedford Mr G had died, and Mrs G was already having doubts about Mabel, so she didn't introduce me to her for some time. When I did meet her, she hadn't been told anything about me, and although we got on well she didn't recognise any special family connection between us, so nothing much came of it. I was just another shape to be seen around her hive. Nothing special. Later on, the guardian had written to Mabel to see if she had recognised me as a relation, but Mrs Goodwin had intercepted the letters (as she often did) and then found out more about my childhood, including that my nickname was "Luggy." So that was how she had called me "Luggy Andrews girl" when she had been casting out demons in Mrs G's house; she hadn't been able to see things through special powers, just been able to read letters not meant for her. It also turned out that my surname probably wasn't really "Andrews" at all. My father, the man with a moustache, was called Andrew, but no-one would officially recognise him as my father. Before she died, my mother had held me tight and said: "My Etholle.....name her Etholle.....Andrew's." Or perhaps Mrs Fox had just imagined that bit of the story.

From then on, I had become known as Etholle Andrews as they thought she had said the father's surname was Andrews, and as I never had a Birth Certificate, it was never questioned. All because of an apostrophe! When I told Meg all this she thought it hilarious, much better than the ubiquitous 'Greengrocers' aberrant apostrophe' she said. She did try to explain it all to me, but I still ate'n't sure.

One day, Hilda Green of all people turned up at the door and was very nice to me and said they would love it if I went to the services again. Oh, and could I do a bit of typing in the offices, as they were busy and needed help. Of course I said yes, though it was a couple of years till I went regularly. It would be a bit of company for me. They needed me now, but was I a doormat? Anyway, I started going again and I must say it did make me feel better. Mr Coghill was a keen photographer and took us on trips around the town to take cine pictures as well. He must have been quite well off as they were very expensive. On the films some of the members really played up to the camera, looking cheerful and happy though afterwards they were serious again. Someone arranged a photograph to be taken of the whole Campus from an aeroplane! It made a lovely picture. I don't know how it's possible for aeroplanes to fly but they do.

To be honest, there's a lot of things, like flying, that people just accept but I simply don't understand. I don't see how Electricity works: by flicking a switch how can this power flow to a light bulb and make it light up? And however can a wireless work? That's even more ridiculous. Some kind of Magic, I think. And how DO plants grow then die and then grow again the next year? And however can anyone be resurrected from the dead and live again? I don't understand things that others take for granted. So I started to think that if unbelievable things like electricity worked because you believed it would work, then perhaps the things the Panaceans believed in could also be true. You just had to believe.

Looking at my diaries, I started to see the members regularly and go to services, but no one said I should become a full member.They were happy to have me make the numbers up, so to speak. In fact you almost forgot that it was a religious group. I went to the Annual Meetings. There was hardly any talk about Mrs Barltrop as God's Daughter. The Healing Mission also seemed a bit of a fraud. I remember I was there in 1960 when they discussed whether to buy a new supply of the Healing Linen as they thought they were running out. They talked for a long while but I don't think they bought any in the end. But the point was, if they HAD bought some, it wouldn't have worked, as it wouldn't have had the breath of Mrs Barltrop on it! Obvious really, as she had died 26 years before. But no one said that, and even Mr Rasmussen just sat there and said nothing. He should have known better. In fact, he seemed to distance himself from what was going on, always finding ways to turn down offers of more responsibility. Dilys was the same. They wanted her to become the leader I think, but she was having none of it. She wanted to be left alone. Mr Temple tried to be more active, but they always turned down chances to have free publicity in newspapers, preferring to put their own advertisements for the Healing or the Box to be opened.

As time went by the atmosphere just changed, and we could do more of what we liked. Nowadays, there aren't many of us anyway, and most of us can't do much. Without the servants most of them would be useless, but I can still get about. I suppose it started when Mrs Goodwin and Hilda Green died, as they were the ones who everyone was a bit scared of. They just had that thing about them, a feeling of authority, that made you think you had to do whatever they said. A bit like how a schoolmaster gets you to do things just by looking. In 1942, Mrs Goodwin (as the Divine Mother) said that everyone who smoked must voluntarily give up, and if they didn't, she would set a date for smoking to be banned completely. Luckily for some, she died before the date came. Peter carried on ploughing a lonely furrow, living in his own world, a lonely world I think. He was the last of the original followers and only he really knew what things were like at the beginning, before Eden went wrong.

I once sat near him in the sunshine at the side of the chapel, looking at Yggdrasyl. I didn't know if he was talking to me or to himself, but he went on for several minutes. He said we were once like a ship heading out to sea, for a certain destination, in calm waters and with full crew. Now we were in a boat that had lost its rudder, with torn sails, no oars, and the sextant lost overboard. It was so sad. Everyone respected him, called him Peter, not Mr Rasmussen, but Peter, as he had been Mrs Barltrop's Rock. He was normally so serious, but I think he just felt abandoned. So sad. He kept on as the senior member, but didn't bother to try and take over, just left things to others who didn't do things as well as he might have done. Another time, a little before he died, I went to see him but he was just rambling on, quoting the Bible randomly and not making sense. Then he stopped, stared into space and whispered firmly, "I would have walked over hot coals for her, hot coals, slept on a bed of nails for her, walked on dangerous thin ice for her, on razor blades for her, over hot coals. I would have had no fear with her beside me. Nothing else would have mattered. Nothing matters. All sparks must burn out in the end."

135

When I told my neighbour Gary that, he said it sounded a bit dodgy – he must have been sniffing around Mabel. After all, it seemed strange that he had wanted to sleep in a cold attic to be close to her. Perhaps he had had the occasional midnight sleepwalk down to her bedroom ...and her son Adrian had had his suspicions as well. But I think it was just him wanting to have a mother figure in his life, the mother love he perhaps never had, being a good son but without the complications. Or on the other hand it might be unrequited love for a woman he loved, and sometimes unrequited love is the best love of all as it lasts forever, like a mother's for a child. He was strange, but nobody had a bad word for him.

Like Mr Rasmussen said, they were like a ship without a rudder. They relied on me more and more as I was quite active still, whereas many of them were old. It was getting like an Old People's Home, and those who were more active treated it as a Social Club. They got members from other parts of the country to move here, so the houses would be occupied, to keep the numbers up. The houses were mostly in a poor state to live in as they were cold, with no hot water and no modern appliances. It was like they were still living in the world of 1914. The world had passed them by.

I was far more modern than the rest of them. Mrs G had seen no reason to be uncomfortable in her home, so there were proper appliances to help me. My neighbours became good friends and looked after me if I was ill and pushed me into getting things like a good electric fire and cooker. They kept me up to date with things I'd not heard about. I heard a lot of shouting one day and went round to find that they were watching football on their television. It was wonderful. In colour as well! They were so excited that they made me come round a few days later to see the Final of the World Cup. England won. People in the street were running and jumping and shouting and cheering. They were so happy, and so was I! At the service that night I talked to the others about it but no one cared. If I sat in my back garden I could hear what was going on in the Clancys' garden, and I got to know about Radio Caroline and Radio London and I would sing along to the tunes. If they thought I was lonely, they invited me into their home to see some television programmes. They liked 'The Prisoner' and I'm sure they kept looking at me when it was on but I don't know what it was all about. I remember seeing 'Alice in Wonderland' at Christmas 1966 and I could understand why Mrs Barltrop had liked it. I wanted it to come on again but it never did.

Etholle
The Fun We Had

———▷•◆•◁———

Now, in 1976, as I look back at what I've written I can see that it all looks a bit gloomy, life in the Society. But it wasn't all like that, so I think I should mention some other things that struck me as funny or interesting. So here's thoughts about The Fun We Had. Actually, it's strange how things work out, because some of my clearest memories are of little things that made me happy.

An outsider might think that we were all a miserable lot, too serious and thinking about things that most people aren't aware of, thinking about all those things I never understood anyway. Yes, the days did normally drag along, doing pointless things like writing instructions on this that or the other, and having to do it over and over again as we hadn't got it quite right, and then finding out afterwards that other people in other rooms had been doing exactly the same work as we had, but no one knew. I sometimes thought that they just gave us things to do to keep us out of mischief – the Devil might find work for idle hands after all.

Anyway, even when we were on top of the world, on the crest of a wave, and everything seemed so serious, we still had fun at times. There were the simple things, but sometimes there were the hilarious ones that shouldn't have happened, mainly when Evelyn was around. She could be a right stirrer, and so cheeky with it. I wish she had spent more time with me, I really do. At the start it was just the official things that they gave us to enjoy, but we did things in secret as well.

After all, how much fun can you have in the Wireless Room? Not a lot really. A room with a radio, a dart board, piano, and cards, but not much more. The people there kept with their own, paying no attention to me and talking to each other quietly and whispering sometimes and looking around and not saying anything interesting and just doing …

nothing much. They weren't sure why I was there, and nor was I.

The Garden Parties were better though, and sometimes fun. Everything was arranged by Mrs Barltrop down to the last detail, especially when we had members from all over the country arrive for the Annual Meetings, and I must say that she treated them very well. One year, 1930 I think it was, a lovely July day, we had games in the garden at the Haven: Clock Golf, Potato Race, Golf Croquet, Hooks and Rings, Throwing the Dart, and best of all, the Country Dancing. I remember we did Helston Fury, Sellengers Round, Bo Peep, Rufty Tufty, Jenny Pluck Pears and others as well. We didn't do my favourite though, Black Nag. I joined in with some, and those I wasn't in I still danced anyway, twizzling about round the corner and waving my arms around with no one seeing me. It was a wonderful time, perfect, and everyone was so grateful to be there in the Garden of Eden. Then there was a buffet at 4, then tea afterwards, and before the meeting Miss Broad played the piano. All the tables were set out saying who had to sit where, and Mrs G made me sit near her as if I was important, because she was on a table close to the top and I wondered if I might take home one of the balloons they had put up and I didn't listen too much to what was being said because I was so excited to be there.

We had a lovely time, though I heard from Amy afterwards that Mrs Barltrop wasn't too happy with the way some things went. She wrote down all the things that were wrong, and I believe she was quite cross about it as things had to be just so and perfect: the servants should have dressed better, the meringues were difficult to eat, the lemonade was too weak, the table looked flat and ugly, there should have been a different choice of sandwich, and the cake was vulgar. Well, I though it was all very nice actually.

Another year, she arranged a performance of bits from Alice in Wonderland. Amy had forgotten to get some things from town, and I happened to be going so I said I'd get them. Mrs Barltrop was grateful for me offering. I was her saviour she said! I bought flowers from Laxtons for 7/8, two combs (5d) and some perfume (3 ½ d) from Braggins and 18 shillings worth of fruit from Dix in Silver Street.

In Laxtons and Dix I told them who it was for, and they said they'd make sure it was delivered straight away as they might be sent to Hell if they forgot. At the performance, most people laughed and smiled but it confused me as that was before I had read the book. It was a load of nonsense really, but it was funny to see them all dressed up. Evelyn was funny and definitely the best, pretending to be a dormouse and as the White Rabbit. I think she was the best actor, especially when she looked cheekily at me rubbing her rabbit ears and grinning. Miss Broad was scary in her costume and I didn't like her at all. Afterwards Mrs G told me in her way that The March Hare and the Hatter were both mad, and that the rest of them might be as well, and that Alice lived in a different world, where she thought she was the only sensible one there, but couldn't control what was going on, and that Mr Carroll was a very clever writer, and although it was a children's book I should read it as some children's books have grown up meanings as well. So I did.

We often went to the pictures. Saturday nite at the Granada, the Plaza, the 'drome! To see my favourite celluloid heroes! There were plenty in the town though there was one that we weren't supposed to go to, but eventually I did. One day after the war, Evelyn said we should go to see Robert Donat in "Goodbye Mr Chips" and I didn't realise which cinema it was till we got there, but before I could say anything she grabbed my arm and pulled me in. I remember the seats were a warm blue colour.

We both felt guilty being in the dark together, doing something we shouldn't together, and enjoying ourselves together.

It was a lovely story, about an old schoolteacher who had a sad life with glimpses of happiness in between the disappointments, but who eventually dies remembering the happy times. In the bit where Robert Donat's beautiful wife Greer Garson died, Evelyn held my hand and we both cried. It was so sad. Mr Chips said he tried to make sure his pupils had a sense of proportion and a sense of humour, because if they had those things, they could take on anything. At the end, we both had tears in our eyes again, and I had to give her a long hug as she wanted me to make her feel better and I kissed her on the forehead. I can still remember the smell of the scent behind her ear, and the way she made a final little sniff before saying we should go in case anyone had seen us together. It was an exciting adventure that made us both sad and happy at the same time, one of those perfect moments that you know will never happen again, but wish they could.

It was the best day of my life.

Many of my happiest times were with Evelyn, especially if Dilys was there as well, though only if it was the nice Dilys. Twice I was able to go out on the missions to bury the blessed linen at the points of the compass of the Royal Domain. Normally there would be Mr Boddington to dig the hole, one of the Apostles to put it in water and say the words, Dilys to put it in the ground, and Evelyn (as the Head Gardener) to cover it up. Mr Boddington was a nice fat man who we liked a lot, and Evelyn made fun of him, which he liked. He often wore a checked suit, and Evelyn said that it was well known that the fatter the man the bigger the checks. A little later talk was that he killed himself, but hardly anyone spoke about the reason, and pretended he had just died.

One All Hallows Eve, we were told to take Divine Protection cards to five churches in the town. We pretended we were spies on a secret mission, hiding in the shadows, then running in the darkness to another shadow till we reached each church. We would go in, sprinkle the water and hide a card somewhere so no-one would find it. Most people took it so seriously, but Evelyn and me couldn't stop giggling when they weren't looking.

Best of all, though we only did it once, was when we played at making people jump. By the 1950's the people in Albany Road were used to us, and it was a case of Live and Let Live, but others were scared of us. You might see children walking the road, going to school, and looking warily at some houses. At that time about ten houses in the road were ours: 4 19 25 31 8 10 12 14 16 18 I think. They would walk one side of the road, cross to the other, then cross back again so as not to walk by our houses. Evelyn and I sometimes went to Mr and Mrs Temple's old home at number 7 when it was empty, to check everything was alright. Evelyn as the Society Gardener had to go to all houses from time to time and brought me along to help. We saw two boys of about 13 going cockily along the road, and deliberately going past our houses, pausing outside to show that they weren't afraid of anything. The next day, we went there and Evelyn made a very large dummy like a Guy Fawkes which she put at the front window. We watched the boys coming, and as they stopped outside I pulled back the curtains and Evelyn pushed the dummy so it fell against the window with a noise. The dummy's balloon head went bang and off the boys went. One stopped at the end of the road and looked back, to show he was braver than the other. But we never saw them again.

We were never really cruel to the others, though things they did could be funny without them realising it and you couldn't help laughing. I remember that in about 1956, Peter (who must have been nearly eighty by then) took to riding a motorbike. He bought it from a member called Mr McCulloch who lived away, for twenty pounds and fifteen shillings. He told Evelyn and arranged for it to be sent by train. As she was a good mechanic he got her to get it going and he sorted out insurance. For a while he did putt putt about, very slowly, in the quiet roads but we worried when he went in the direction of the Embankment in case he couldn't stop and went into the river. He seemed to enjoy his short expeditions to nowhere in particular in his own little world, but it was too dangerous. In the end Evelyn did something to make the thing stop working. She told him that there was a problem with the Cotter Pin Spindle Bracket, which meant the flange was out of true so it would be impossible to mend. Peter nodded as if he understood, and went back to his world. I was really impressed that Evelyn knew so much about the terms used in the land of Mechanics, but she said that she had just made it all up and she wouldn't know what a Cotter Pin Spindle Bracket was if it fell on her.

Another lovely time I remember with Evelyn was one very bad winter when the river was iced over. We went for a stroll with Dilys along the Embankment. We were dressed up warm with coats, hats and scarves. As we walked, with Evelyn in the middle, arm in arm in arm, she suddenly laughed and said "Will you do as I say?" We both said yes. "Let's do Icyskidskis!" she shouted, then dragged us both to the riverbank, where we saw children playing and skating on the thick ice. We walked on the ice, still arm in arm in arm, and none of us were afraid. We skated, we fell over, we laughed aloud, and we didn't have a care in the world. We went back wet, rosy cheeked and electrified by it all. Yet the next day Dilys was in a dark mood again and refused to talk about it even though she must have known it would cheer any normal person up; but she wasn't a normal person. I suggested that we make a snowman on Castleside lawn, but she told me off.

We also had good times when we went to the Country Dancing meetings in the 1950's at the Reading and Recreation Room in Barkers Lane. There were regular events, and the two of us would walk the short distance to the building which was a sort of Village Hall but in a town. It was an old Edwardian building, planned so ordinary people could meet to educate and enjoy themselves. Most of the dancers were our age, and we could still throw ourselves around, reeling with the best of them for a couple of hours, then walk home even more quickly. I could dance the "Black Nag" to my heart's content. Eventually, Evelyn became less keen on going because of age, and as I didn't like to go by myself, it all stopped.

I still walked by there alone on dancing nights to listen to the music, the laughs and to soak up the warmth, standing outside, but it wasn't the same any more.

I wish I could have had more time with Evelyn – and Dilys when in a good state – but things never seemed to work out right. Like her mother, Dilys sometimes just Lost Control and no-one could really help. To try and help her, they sent her to stay in France with the French believers. Evelyn took Dilys there for a long time for her to recover from her illness but I wasn't invited of course, so I had to stay here. When Evelyn lived in Rothsay Road and I was not far away in Castle Road we hardly ever visited each other. Her older sister Muriel was always a more serious person, and I think she disapproved of her younger sister fooling around and being flippant. Muriel was the sensible one and after their mother died, she became like her. So over the years, although we got on like a house on fire, we didn't meet all that much and a lot depended on chance meetings. But those times were very precious. Time well spent is so rare in my life. I just liked being there.

One sad thing was how Dilys got worse. She kept moving from one house to another, ending up a recluse at The Grove. I learnt this from Olga Hughes, who was a nervous shy lady, the kind of person that you never hear anyone saying a bad word about. She kept a diary and I have to admit that I read it once, to see if she wrote things different from the kind I put in mine. Olga moved to 18 Albany Road, alone in such a big house, and she told me about how Mr Rasmussen had sprinkled the holy water in every room of the house and said prayers in a special ceremony on October 19th 1954:

" In the names of the Great Divine Father and Mother Son and Daughter, to whom this four square - this domain belongs

I sprinkle the blessed water into this North-East corner of our domain, and on the landing

Now the top front room of No 18:

In the name of the Father I sprinkle this to the North and in the name of the Mother to the South, and the Son in the East and the Daughter in the West.

I ask that now when this has been accomplished that chaos shall be no more seen here or in our country England or eventually no where on earth.

That thou O God will make Satan the Unjust and Lucifer the Wicked and their accomplices know that their rule here and in all the lands will therefore cease and be no more.

AND THAT THY POWER AND THY RULE COMES INTO VISIBLE OPERATION"

I couldn't help flicking through the pages of the diary. One part of me says that was sinful, but another says it's just what any normal person would do.

From Olga Hughes' Diary
(Excerpts as written 1928-1967)

1928
June 28. Wrote my first report to The Divine Mother on my faults and failings. A report is to be sent in fortnightly.
Sept 5. Received "The Service" for the destruction of my Mortal Soul.
Sept 15. My Mortal Soul was destroyed at 8pm (At the Sand Dunes, Old Hunstanton). Held the service in my bedroom.
Oct4. Received a new Section with a crystal attached and a new formula to be used. The crystal Received the Royal Seal. Belonged to a necklace of Octavia.
Oct 30. Received the Royal Seal.

1940
Feb 2 EG downstairs again. The first time since Christmas Day.
Apr 22 EG downstairs in the afternoon after being 3 weeks upstairs.
Aug 15 Conjunction of Jupiter and Saturn not occurred since the Birth of Christ nearly 2000 years ago.
Aug 29 A clock belonging to Octavia's grandfather which did not go when Octavia had it suddenly struck 10 after Miss Dilys had had the clock for some time about 9.30pm. PR put it right, struck it round the hours and it is still going. 10= a New Beginning.

1947
Aug 11 Miss Dilys slept at no 12 and at present does not wish to return to The Haven. She has left The Haven exactly 21 years after Mrs Firth left (Aug 11 1926).
7 years= 10 minutes:therefore 21 years=half an hour.
(What's all this stuff about 7 years equalling 10 minutes, and so on? Well. Believers in Mabel and the Visitation generally worked out

that according to II Peter 3.8, God had his own Divine chronology, different from the modern one. In it:

God's Working Week	*6000 years*
God's day	*1000 years*
God's hour	*41 years and 4 months*
God's 10 minutes	*7 years approx*
God's minute	*8 months and 10 days*

But sometimes I think they miscalculated).

1948
Mar 1 A dead owl discovered in the Dining Room at Castleside. It was about a fortnight since the room was last entered, when everything was as usual. It had turned the electric light on and had died for want of water.

1949
May 12 83 years and 4 months (1 hour) since Octavia was born (Jan 12 1866)

Aug 22 Went shopping with Miss Dilys to help her buy a frock.

Aug 23 The Divine Mother sent me a message through Miss Dilys. I had been very kind in helping her shop yesterday but I must be moderate in my kindness. Also that the pleasure we both enjoyed could not be maintained permanently yet as we were still in a devil's world.

Oct 22 Miss Dilys pointed out to me that I had not been spiritually alert about a remark she made when we were out shopping on the 19th. Then I made an unfortunate remark that she was more spiritually advanced than I was, which distressed her very much.

1950
Feb 27 Miss Dilys came to Castleside when I was working there and said she had to tell me not to talk too much in the garden to the Miss Keeleys. "Be moderate" was the message. I could talk for a minute or two, but not to let it go on. It would help them as well as me if I did this.

Mar 28 Miss Dilys came over to Castleside this afternoon to tell me when I work at the Haven Eva shuts windows there at 4 o'clock and that I was not to talk beyond a word or two to her, to keep my dignity with her and not let her get familiar.

Apr 4 Miss Dilys came to see me. When working at the Haven, I am to do so in a spirit of meekness and humility and to ask the Divine Mother to guide me to do the work to please Her not myself.

May 4 Miss Dilys came to Castleside and told me that my citadel had been attacked because the Divine Mother does not like my pride in my own capacities.

Aug 3 Miss Dilys told me that I had allowed the mortal mind to come forward on Tuesday while working with her at the Haven. She said it was because I was tired. She reminded me to talk more when with her to avoid thinking .

Aug 23 Miss Dilys told me I must be lead by the Divine Mother and not have ideas of my own on how the work should be done. I am working in that house for discipline and correction. Also for enjoyment in my work- if the mortal mind does not come uppermost.

1951

Sept 4 Mrs Vyse arrived at the Haven to turn out Dilys' room. D came over to see how things were going and when she found her room dismantled she was in a terrible state and said I could not possibly know what I had done to her by taking down her pictures etc. I had taken away the last things she possessed and now she had nothing.

Oct 2 Went for a short walk with Dilys in the afternoon as nurse could not take her. She was in a very distressed frame of mind and would not stay out long.

1952

Feb 7 Dilys came to my room at bedtime and gave me a very serious talk. She said I was very nervy, I was draining her vitality, making her frightfully tired, I concentrated on her too much, was too earnest. In fact my nerves were in such a rotten state I was no good for anything-

I must pull myself together. I am over anxious and anxiety is a sin. I must tone down words, actions, etc.

1954

Nov 6 Miss Dilys said she did not want to have anything more to do with me. She had LEFT the Society and was considering leaving Bedford.

Nov 15 D came round to see me at 8.45 pm to get things off her mind so as to get peace. She told me no one here had caused her so much suffering and misery as I had. It made me see how terribly self important and aggressive I am. When she left she said that she could forgive me and that she felt better.

Nov 20 D came again as all had not been cleared up. As she was going I said "you haven't stayed so long this time." The next day I had the most distressing and upsetting letter from her denouncing everything about me, my mind, my self, my pride saying she would not come round again until I could go to her in true penitence for all the misery I have always caused her and that she could not forgive me.

Nov 25 Had a very kind and comforting letter from D and full of Teaching. She explained fully all her distress and suffering at the hands of the members of P.S. Her whole life has been full of suffering and sorrow and only God to go to for comfort.

1959

Aug 10 Mr Temple and Mrs Lloyd both sent a letter to Dilys' brother in Canada about her condition, which is getting very serious. He was asked not to tell her.

Aug 15 Had a most awful scene with D at the office- she found out that I had had something to do with sending the letter. She has now finished with me and all and will have nothing more to do with us.

Aug 18 Dilys left No 9 and returned to 36A The Grove.

Aug 28 Very unhappy about D. Wrote a letter of apology about the letter to Canada as Mrs L and I feel we should not have sent it as things turned out so badly.

1960

Aug 5 Just as I was about to leave the office in the afternoon Dilys suddenly burst in and screamed at me about my evil being laid upon her and she denounced it. Mrs Lloyd was with her and D stormed at both of us for about half an hour. Mr Temple finally came down the stairs and soon afterwards D left in a somewhat quieter mood. What it was all about I hardly know.

Aug 7 A petition up to the Divine Mother for Dilys' release signed by PR, Mrs Lloyd, Mrs Cuthbertson, Miss M Gillett and myself.

Aug 14 Dilys returned to No 9 for meals and to sleep.

Sept 10 Had a very terrible interview with Dilys in the office- she swore and cursed me. I walked away and she followed me to No 18, but I would not see her. Then when she went she rang both front and side door bells and knocked but I would not answer. In the afternoon I received a note from her which rather inferred that she knew she had gone too far.

Sept 11 Dilys called at 12.45 am to make it up and brought a peach as a peace offering!

Sep 27 Had a very stormy interview with Dilys at the office. After tea she called at no 18 and we made it up and she went away quite happy.

Sept 28 Dilys' birthday. She spent a very happy day and went out with Mrs Lloyd, Mrs Cuthbertson. She sent me a nice message thanking me .

1962

Sept 9 Dilys unexpectedly came to see me as I was cooking the dinner. She stayed about half an hour. We had a nice quiet chat. Nearly 2 years since I have spoken to her.

Sept 10 D M B came round about 7pm and asked me out to supper but I did not go- Bath Night the excuse!

1967

Oct 6 Mr Temple very unwell and very vague.

Oct 15 Dilys had a slight stroke.
          Mr Temple removed to hospital.

Oct 17 Mr Temple passed over
　　　　Dilys went into hospital.
Oct 24 Mr Temple's funeral.
Nov 4　Visited Dilys in hospital.
Nov 18 The £ devalued.

1968
16 July Dilys died

Etholle
In Every Eden a Heartache

Although I had been spending more time at the Society and learning more about it, I was more interested in my neighbours and the wonderful things I started to learn about the world – the world I had missed out on in the last 60 years. Gary took over the house next door in about 1968, when he came back from university, and had a lovely wife called Meg. She was something they called a "hippy" and she dressed in flowery dresses and didn't care what people thought of her. I thought she might be embarrassed to talk to an old woman like me if I bumped into her in the street, but no, she went out of her way to chat with me. "You don't have to be young or have long hair to think like a hippy" she told me and she was right. Although I was much older, I found that the things they talked about were things I agreed with when I sat and thought about it. She had studied Sociology, which was something I'd not heard of, but when we chatted I found it interesting, and she lent me some books I ought to read. I didn't completely understand all the long words but Meg explained. I owed so much to them, and still do. For Christmas once, she bought me one of the long flowery dresses she liked. I wore it a lot and as I strolled down the road she would shout out of the window "Swing them hips, Eth! Go and show 'em. We'll get you a man yet." She's always optimistic.

Once, she put a sign in her window saying "Sister, Angela, you're welcome in this house." I don't know why. Gary said it was a noble thought but hoped it wouldn't be necessary.

What made us close was the day she had their baby. Gary was away when Meg called to me to come and help. An ambulance was coming but she was in pain and wanted me to stay with her. It was horrible but wonderful. I'd never been anywhere near a pregnant woman before, and it was strange to see how someone could be fearful but so happy at the same time. It was a feeling she had that I think I can never have. I was a big help to her, though I have to say that the first thing that came into my mind was to say "Yowling won't help."

They thought up lots of strange names for the baby, not normal ones but names like Ocean, Dweezil, Sky, Smiles and Papers. I suggested Felicity (I've always thought of myself as a Felicity) and told them, yes I was quite firm about this, I told them that a person's name can shape their whole life so it must be carefully given. In the end, they named her Eve, thought when she was about 14 she decided to call herself Lilith. Later, they had a son as well.

There were things that happened to upset me at that time and finally make me give up trying to do my bit to help the Panaceans. Evelyn died in 1975. At the time she was back living at 19 Rothsay Road, and although I hadn't been invited, I went to see her to see how she was, as her sister Muriel had died just before Christmas the previous year. She was so glad to see me, but it was sad to find her in such a lost state of mind. She'd just bought a fresh car though she was in no state to drive it. CPL593H it was. She had sorted out things that were important to her now that she realised she would soon be going as well. Most of her possessions were to do with the Society, such as rules, instructions and prayers, but she also had a few things from her childhood. There was a small scrapbook of drawings and stories she had made up, though they stopped after she was about 7. One was the tale of how once she had a nightmare when she saw her mother cramming her shoes with peas.

She showed me the scrapbooks she and Muriel had made, with pictures and newspaper cuttings of Bedford life through the decades, things like the R101 crash and visits from Royalty. They were very neat and well set out. There was a short novel she had written soon after she came to Bedford, called "The House of Waiting," which was dedicated to her friend Dilys. She told me that she had once been friendly with a young man and they had both wanted to spend more time together, but Mrs Goodwin had forbidden them to see each other. In fact the young man was Mrs Goodwin's son. She kept receipts for work carried out to the house years before: Two pounds eighteen and nine in November 1970 for carpentry work – why keep it? She kept a list of things she had willingly left when she was moved from The Grove back to Rothsay Road; she left virtually everything including furniture, and the only thing she wanted to keep was a garden hosepipe.

She showed me her confessions that she had admitted years before and I realised that the happy-go-lucky woman I had admired and loved being with had for years been browbeaten into thinking she had so many faults that she came to believe she was useless. She even thought that her mother had brought the sisters to the Society so that they would not live in the normal world. They were rich, so she could have had a nice life of luxury and ease, but instead she had to abide by rules and restrictions not far off like being in a prison. She just became institutionalised.

Her "faults," which she confessed to Dilys, were quite separate from her official confession, and went to 9 pages of large paper. And how ridiculous they were:

I walk strangely

I talk in a strange way

I do not wear clean clothes

My speech is crude, sometimes suggestive with men

I always make excuses

Everything bores me

I say awkward embarrassing things at meals

I monopolise the wireless

I like Irene more than anyone else

I interrupt other people's conversations

I am too abrupt

I don't like muddy walks

I fidget a lot

I am quarrelsome over small things

I frighten Dilys when in the car

I smell

I have an idiotic smile

I have impure thoughts
I get depressed
I am self-important
I am too sympathetic to others
I am not sympathetic enough to others
I screw up my shoulders
I go out without carrying a handbag
I wear the wrong shoes for meetings
I am too eager to take sweets
I copy Dilys' dress
I am too fond of Praise
I make too much noise when eating
I don't like the Fonteinbleau Operas
I am offhand with older people
I want my way in all things
I am quarrelsome
I am objectionable
I make too much fuss if I have a cold
Muriel was put to write a long report on me, but I can't remember the contents
I am in a hopeless condition.

And there was much more like that load of tosh. I could hardly believe that the lively person I had always looked forward to seeing, and wanted to see more of, had been in such a sad state of mind all along. I wish I could have saved her from the Nothing she'd become.

When I got home I closed my eyes and thought of all the good happy times I had had in her company and decided to write them down, because if I don't, I may forget them and they will be lost forever. All those wonderful moments lost, that we'll never find again.

Other things upset me about the Society as well. I went to several more Annual Meetings, and still all they talked about was repairs to their properties, or whether to buy this property or that, and difficulties with tenants. There was still hardly any talk about the original purpose

154

they were there, but if someone tried to do things they told them off, like Mrs Blumenthal, who wrote to the Queen about the Box. They told off Miss Owen for cutting some long branches off Iggdrasill without reference to the Garden Committee. How stupid. They counted the number of world disasters so they could tell everyone at the Meetings. They listed floods, earthquakes, rail and aeroplane crashes, explosions, fires and riots of all types and gave a final total. This was supposed to show that the Millennium must be close, but I don't see how.

How petty it all was.

They were also far too obsessed with things to do with money. I don't think they were misers or con-men, but everything had to be done in a certain secretive way. Although they had lots of money, they didn't always pay their bills. I remember that sometime in the 1970's I went to pay my Electricity bill and overheard a staff member talking about the Society. She said that they always had to keep ringing them as they never paid till the last moment every time. Colonel Graham did try to make them more sensible over money matters. He was a member, though his wife thought it was all daft. Miss Green and the others didn't like him at all. She once ordered him out of the offices because he had opened an investment without her permission. My oh My, was she angry! The investments were confusing - he talked about British Transport 3% stock 1978/88, 6% funding stock 1993, 14% Treasury stock 1998/2001, and 5 ½ Consolidated Funding stock. How complicated, but he seemed to know his stuff. There was an account opened with Nationwide Building Society, through their agent, Gordon's, and a while after they opened a branch in town so we went there to place a protection card. The signature in the book looked like a Mr Dickerson, and we wondered if he worked there. Col Graham and I crept in and went into a little alcove at one side where we couldn't be seen, and decided to put the card behind a metal heating rail. As we did so, two customers came in and said to the lady on the till "We've got an appointment with Mr Dickerson, *The Holy Man*." A few moments later a large man with a beard came down some stairs, shook hands with the customers, who called him Barry, and they disappeared. Well, our money was to be protected not just by the protection card, but by *The Holy Man*! Our money was Safe Inside Nationwide.

Miss Green and others didn't like Col Graham because they let it be known they thought he was a womaniser, but they could only have known that if it was in his confessions, and they were supposed to be secret.

Getting on so well with the neighbours set me thinking about how silly and unfair the Panaceans were to each other. They didn't have the same kind of affection that Gary and Meg showed me. Yes, they loved their Octavia, they loved their Divine Mother, and they loved their little world, but now it all seemed even more unnatural than ever. Mabel had only occasionally shown any real love for her children, and had hardly been aware when aunt Fanny died. When Adrian had visited he had to live away from his family home. The married couples hardly seemed to be married. Their children often preferred to live far away. They loved the idea of Octavia, but not Mabel herself. And then there was the embarrassing thing about sex. Now I'd never thought about this before, but their whole attitude to human relationships was not normal. Some of the women had crushes on each other, and had to admit it in their confessions. I'm sure of that.

I'm glad I never had to make a confession.

Even if members were married, they seem to have the idea that it should only be to have children, not for anything else. "Kissing is forbidden even between man and wife inside of HQ because it produces evil sensations and results in sex." They were like nuns, married to their belief, not to a human.

At that time, there were several break-ins at The Haven and Castleside. The buildings had to be checked regularly and I was on the rota to do this some days. On one occasion they told me it was my fault that a break-in hadn't been spotted earlier, as I was late going round the building. They really made me feel small and useless. Gary happened to go past the building and he called the police and sorted things out, as I was in no state to do anything. I just sat there on the ground, staring at a record he had just bought at the shop in Allhallows.

I suppose I was useless really, but they had no reason to have a go at me like that, and I told myself that I'd give them one more chance to be charitable towards me, at the service that night. If they were horrible or ignored me, then I'd have nothing more to do with them.

Later on, Gary heard rumours that the break-ins were by some young teenagers from Waterloo Road who did it for a dare, as part of a rite of passage, to go and sleep in the "house of witches" where all was dusty and forgotten like in Miss Haversham's room. He said they were harmless boys who accidentally broke a couple of things and just needed a clip round the ears and would probably grow up into well balanced people.

"Unlike the Panaceans" I could hear Mrs G saying in my ear.

Etholle
Break-in 1975

I gave my statement to the policemen, who were very nice and patient with me, what with my crying and sniffling all the time. They said they'd keep a look-out for burglars in the area, but didn't expect to find the culprits. They virtually wrote the statement for me. I suppose I didn't really make much sense as I was so upset, and talking drivel. But afterwards, I thought I'd better write down how I REALLY felt that day - the day that Castleside was broken into, and the Panaceans blamed me for not spotting it earlier. So here's the statement I could have given to them.....

My day had started well, getting up early as there was a fresh Spring feel to the world, the kind of day that musn't be wasted. Never mind that I'd probably wasted loads of days like this before, this might be a good day. In the end it wasn't, but in some ways it was an important day.

My job was to check the outside of the big building, the important place. Most people don't know this, but it's a large Victorian house, originally someone's (large) home but then converted to a Boarding House for boys at the school. Future soldiers, diplomats, rogues and even loving fathers once stayed there while their parents had gone to India, Africa or further on Imperial business, or just to get rich. But to the Community, this is the most important place in the world. The place where the Box will be opened, where secrets will be revealed, and the door opened to the coming of the Lord. This is where St John's revelations will at last become a reality and the believers will have everlasting life in their earthly heaven. The garden itself is Eden. The early followers worked this out from the Bible and writings that I've never actually seen myself, but it must be true. Mabel never denied it, when others had revealed this truth, and surely the glory of the garden itself disproves deniers.

Oh the policemen wouldn't have appreciated all those details would they! They'd have thought I was as barmy as the rest of them. I'll carry on...

I loved making my slow patrol round the building – just the outside, as the inside isn't freely available to just anyone. All was in order ...the lean-to potting shed ....the fish pond ....the side windows (curtains arranged so no one can see the treasure inside) ...the front door. I went up the step to the door. I love the metal sign at the right side: "Only ring if an answer is required" it reads. Silly. Why would anyone ring otherwise? And at the left side, scratched into the brickwork, I always look at the letter "M." I often think that this could have been scratched by Mabel herself, not by some mischievous schoolboy, wanting to leave his mark on his world, to last for as long as the building itself lasts. Perhaps this was an heretical thought so I've never pointed it out to anyone. But it did make me have a silent chuckle. I like to chuckle you know, though I don't dare to do too much of that sort of thing. People might be watching me.

But I'd better get back to what I saw...

Then I went round the other side. But this was when I saw that the building had been broken into. A window was smashed. Was it Burglars? Hooligans? Unbelievers? Communists? Satan himself? I just didn't know what to do. What *Do* people do? I shouted out I think, but it just came out as a tiny bleating noise. I remember falling to the ground as I thought I was paralysed. I shut my eyes. Perhaps that might help. How could anyone harm this place? Would I be blamed? So and so was supposed to have checked the building last night ....or had it been my job? I couldn't remember.

More bleating ...God would help ...surely ....he would know it hadn't been my fault ......I've been a good and faithful servant, please Lord ....what should I do ?...the shame of it, the terrible shame .. I didn't know what to do.

I remember that just then I heard a voice:

" Are you alright Eth? Can I help you up? You seem very upset, and

161

I don't like people to be upset."

I looked up, thinking that someone was going to help me, perhaps an angel. Now I know you'll think that is silly, but if you are as upset as I was then you'll clutch at any straw available, no matter how unlikely.

But in fact, kneeling down beside me on the gravel was no heavenly angel, but still an angel, a Good Samaritan. The Bible was right, for in my time of despair a good person had come to help me. I vaguely recognised that it was my neighbour, Gary. He wasn't from the Community but was from outside. As usual he was scruffily dressed and unshaven but was a man with a kind face that I know I can trust. He was genuine. Sincere. He had a Good Heart. I know that for sure.

" That's kind of you ......I don't know what to do?" That's exactly what I said. I'm sure of that bit.

I let Gary take over and he called the Police, made me comfortable, took me home and made me a strong cup of tea. He and his wife Meg called round three more times that day to chat to me and see how I was after the shock.

No one from the Panacea Society called or asked about how I was.

Yes, that's a better statement than just giving the bare facts. And it was an important day, as it confirmed that the Panaceans didn't really care about me.

And another bonus is that I've managed to use the word "drivel" in a proper way! - Mrs G would have been proud of me.

Etholle
The Chosen 1975

I remember that day at the chapel. I remember looking around at them all. I wrote my thoughts down that night.

They are old, those who are left. Old in every way. The room is old, the air is old, and they are old. Not quite decrepit, but worn out.

The chapel is quiet, with the silence of people who feel that noise would be a sin. To speak would be an embarrassment to them, so they stare at the floor, hands together at their knees as if in prayer, others daydreaming and some with blanked minds. An occasional shuffling of feet, a glance up and forward to look at the window. The Jerusalem window, our Mother Jerusalem above.

The two men are small and wizened, desiccated and dried up like old fruit now past its best. Not much sign of life in there. The six women are smaller and more frail. Not "slim" – that's a polite term. Those in the congregation are thin, like the congregation itself. The gathering used to be vibrant, optimistic, and full. They once hurried to be here by six o'clock each day, to see her, to hear her, and her words. Now they hurry only slowly, needing help from the more-able bodied. There will be more today, but it takes time to walk from the houses further away from Eden. There are now only a few of them left in the world, still waiting.

The men wear rough woollen suits fashionable 25 years ago, brown or navy stripes. Striped ties in a single Windsor knot, not done well, as if rushed by someone too young to care or too old be be capable of a better result. Shoes well polished, though. Haircuts traditional. Short Back and Sides is the right form for a House of God. Always has been and always will be – shows Respect and Discipline. One has the proper male parting on the left, and a touch of Brylcreem. The other has longer grey hair, brushed over to hide baldness. Both have hair in the wrong places, coming out of their ears and noses - not many but enough for people to notice them. As men get old, hair disappears from the right places and goes to the wrong ones. Teeth missing, or false. Heads turned towards the speaker, Thank God at least one ear still works.

The chapel has a fusty smell.

The women are dressed as if from 20 years ago. Long woollen skirts below the knee, cardigans buttoned up, and patterned or floral blouses. Shoes are sensible, some wear brown sandals that are comfortable to the point of being worn out. Very dark tights, nothing light or shiny here of course. Soon they will get out the woollen ones for the winter. None of them have a full set of teeth, and one with false teeth involuntarily moves her jaws about like a cow chewing the cud. Long straggly grey hair, but shorter hair would have made them look younger. Most of them have hats that they have now put on the chairs at the back. Some of these are decorated with flowers round the rim, so they give a cheeriness contrasting with the starkness of the building itself. Their clothes have a definite smell of Lavender, that dependable smell, the smell from chests of drawers from long ago, in houses from long ago, a Time not so long ago. They smell of Eau de Cologne. 4711. A fresh, clean smell.

From the back, I looked at them all. On the face of it I was as compliant as they were, but I had never fully given up my mortal mind and personality, so had never been a full member.

This was supposed to have been a place special for women. The female Messiah, the female child of God, the place of the Divine Mother. But they had never had the chance to do anything much. They had never fallen in love, never gone to university, never felt the kick inside, never really lived. Or loved. They had just lived by a number of rules and restrictions in a limited world that few could remember why or how it had been made so. I had known Mabel, and Mrs Goodwin who had followed her, but after Peter had died I was one of the few left with a direct knowledge of the early days, or at least had not been chosen to have dementia.

164

I remember I was in my own little world. I opened the Bible at Genesis, and read the comforting words to myself, till the doubts went away. Genesis. The Beginning of it all. Such a wonderful word, as are so many of the names in the Old Testament. From Genesis to Revelation. Genesis. I thought of the conversation I'd had not long before with my neighbour Gary, who had been my Good Samaritan at the time of the break-in. He had been so kind and helped me in my distress, whereas the other members had blamed me. In my state of panic, he had tried to turn my attention to things other than the burglary – the books and records he had dropped when kneeling down to help me. I remember that I had seen the name Genesis on the record cover, and thought it must be a sign from God. Silly. I can see that now.

I thought of the strange figures on the front cover, a plump woman old before her time and holding an umbrella. There were two rows of figures dancing, but somehow they were lifeless automata. The main figure was a sleeping man with auburn hair. He was the lawnmower, lying on a bench, in a formal garden, but ignoring or cowering from the party going on around him. The plump woman seemed to be kindly offering one hand out to him to help, but the woman's other hand was black. What did the artist mean by that?

I remember looking up at the Mother Jerusalem window. I heard Little Ben strike, and with the other Panaceans there, I waited for the service to begin.

"Citizens of Hope and Glory

Time goes by – it's the Time of your Life"

were the words to one of the tracks on the record. Well, I'd lived here for the last 55 years – had it been the Time of my Life?

Fragile people.

Old, all of them. From a different time.

Etholle
Saddos, Weirdos and Social Inadequates

I don't know why, but Meg spent lots of time with me, or perhaps I should say on educating me. Although I was older than her it was as if she was the wise mature person helping a teenager to grow up in the ways of the modern world. In some ways I almost became an older sister to little Eve and then to Gus, who followed later. I still looked quite young and felt young. I was still slim, I still had my long auburn hair half way down my back, and apart from it going slightly grey I could do a passing resemblance to a young Vanessa Redgrave from the back, or so Meg claimed. She took me to see 'Mary Queen of Scots' and I must say that there was a resemblance. I felt that I was growing younger, not older.

From the start, Meg and Gary told me I must let myself into their home whenever I wanted company. I'd told them that at the beginning of my diary for 1967 I'd written "Lots of things to do this year" though in my ear I could hear Mrs G say "All of them alone this year."

I played with Eve, I kept the place tidy, picked the children up from school if Meg was too busy, and was someone Eve could tell all her troubles to when she was in a mood. She trusted me, and that made me feel wonderful. She still reminds me about things I'd told her years ago but which I'd forgotten. Or perhaps it's Lilith.

Sometimes Meg and Gary called me round on some pretext and on the television there just happened to be a programme that they said I might like to watch with them. They were crafty like that, but it normally meant I had something new and interesting to think about. Once, they told me that men had landed on the moon but I don't know if it was true. At the cinema, I remember she took me to see '2001 A Space Odyssey,'and 'Modern Times' starring Charlie Chaplin, which had been released again years after the first time. I've never laughed so much in my life!

That made me remember a song that one of my guardians used to sing during the war:
" The moon shines bright on Charlie Chaplin.
His shoes are crackin'
for want of blackenin'
And his little baggy trousers
need a-mendin'
before they send him
to the Dardanelles."

It was a sad song, and it made me think of another sad little song that I'd heard Mr Carew-Hunt singing to himself in the garden once, when he thought no one could hear. At first I'd thought he was singing 'Auld Lang's Syne' as it was to that tune:
"We're here because we're here because we're here because we're here .....We're here because we're here because we're here because we're here"

He went on for ages and ages, just singing quietly and looking at the ground, and I felt sorry for him and could forgive him for sometimes shouting at people.

They had loads of books, and left certain ones on the table if they thought I might like them. Once, Meg threw a newspaper at me and with angry tears said "What do you think of this? It's always the same. Always. Always. **Always** the **SAME**" and pointed at a picture in the paper. It was a lovely summer day in 1972, and she was angry and I'd never seen her angry before. The picture was of some poor frightened children screaming as they ran and there were soldiers in the background. One poor girl had had all her clothes burnt off her and was running, screaming, towards the camera. Meg told me they had been bombed with a horrible weapon called napalm that burned people alive and I thought surely a good God couldn't let that kind of thing happen. The Americans or their friends had bombed them because they were Communists, and as Mrs Barltrop thought Communists were the agents of Satan, I wondered whether she would have thought this was a Good Thing.

I still liked to read my favourite magazine, The People's Friend, which let me into a cosy world where everything was nice but after seeing that picture I felt guilty about it.

They had lots of hollyhocks in their garden. They were lovely, but only for a few days, because they flowered at different times and not all at once. And if there was a high wind they just looked bedraggled and a mess so something that should have been beautiful ended up all wrong.

Gary and Meg educated me, and I helped educate their children, especially Eve. She learnt to read and I would get her to read "Alice in Wonderland" to me, as she liked it as well. Whenever she learnt something new, or finished reading a book, she looked like an adult who has just finished a complicated crossword puzzle, and even when she was a teenager she was as lively as a youngster who has just come home after an exciting school trip. I taught her how to knit, and we laughed a lot as we sat there on the comfy sofa, knitting. I always pretended I needed to stretch out my arm to free up more wool in a way that made me nearly hit her in the face, and she dodged it every time.

" Never sit next to Eth when she's knitting!" they all said.

Then she got older all of a sudden, shrugging her shoulders a lot and spending her time being sullen. Or as Meg put it, became a teenager. She was so clever I thought sometimes that she wouldn't be happy till she became too clever for her own good.

The world in Castle Road was changing, mainly for the better, and there were more and more cars around. I remember that the garage once owned by Mr Munday had new owners. Mr Munday's garage sold bicycles when I first came here, then he moved on to motorcycles and sold petrol, then car mechanics became the thing. For a time you could get a taxi if you rang them. Bedford 2631 it was. I once heard a neighbour ring them just after the war, and watched as it came, but it wasn't Joe though. I've never used a telephone, even now. Mr Ives took it over in the end. He'd been in the war, and he often told tales about what he'd done and he had a lovely big Belgian sheepdog. A few years ago I saw young Mr Ives towing away a young lady's car that had broken down in Castle Road, and she was very upset and I remember that I hoped he would be able to mend it for her. And since then, I've often seen them together so perhaps they got together because of the car breaking down, and it all had a happy ending. I often wonder what happened to the people I once knew or met accidentally. I think that most things turn out alright in the end even if they seem scary at the time and make you a bit anxious.

I didn't see Eve much for a while, and then one afternoon I was sitting at Rothsay Road roundabout when I saw a group of rather frightening people stroll slowly towards me. About 15 years old perhaps. They had clothes that were mostly black, their hair was black, they had black boots, long black overcoats and as they got closer I could see they had black colouring round their eyes but their faces were white. I was scared. They sat at the next bench to me and played some music on their machine and they talked to each other and laughed. When I got up to walk home, they got up as well, and followed. I tried not to look back and walked more quickly, trying not to seem afraid. They were big and scary. I walked faster and faster.

They still followed. When I got near home I fell over, and I heard the gang of youths running towards me. I couldn't get up quickly enough, and I felt hands on my shoulders. As I started to whimper someone said gently "Are you ok miss? Let's get you up. Are you hurt? Shall we help you home?" Just then, Eve came out of her house and rushed up to put her arm round me. She led me into her house and all the gang followed. She sat me down and made a cup of tea (that solves most problems, I think) and I noticed that she was also dressed in black.

It turned out that she was now a "Goth' and they met at the roundabout to listen to music and chat. Her friends called her "Lilith" which I though was also a nice name and they all seemed to get on so well. Meg and Gary said that Goths were looked down on by most people, but they were just misunderstood and they were sure that Eve wouldn't turn bad in any way. I told Eve that if they wanted to meet they could come to my house rather than Meg's, just to be friendly, and one cold day she did come with two others to my home as it was a lot warmer than being outside. Eve still got on well with her parents, but I think she was embarrassed to take her friends there, so my house was better. She said most people thought Goths were Saddos, Weirdos and Social Inadequates, but I thought they weren't as scary as they appeared, and didn't do me any harm, so we should Live and Let Live.

Eve had a friend called Caragh, a lovely, thoughtful girl with a well-chosen name. She became Lilith's best friend. They often did their English homework at my house and I helped, of course. Eve liked Keats, Gerard Manley Hopkins and Edward Thomas; Lilith said she liked to wander about the cemetery with Yeats, Auden and another Thomas. Caragh and Lilith used to tease their teacher by writing dark stories that should have made him worried about their well-being, writing about morbid twists and goings-on in the playground, but all he did was to call their bluff and give them top marks. Strangely, even when they were older and dressed all in black, they would go to town and buy a new "My Little Pony" for their collections. It just goes to show you shouldn't judge by appearances, I suppose.

They came from time to time, though not so much lately. Eve comes by herself a lot now, but before, I would leave them alone and go next door as they appreciated the privacy to do whatever they liked. In fact, I much preferred Meg's house, as it had some very cosy little rooms with comfy old chairs which you could settle in and go to sleep. They had pictures and ornaments that they picked up from car boot sales, and all sorts of curious things that I loved. Best of all was the budgie. He lived in a cage in the conservatory and although he didn't speak, he always looked as if he might. From time to time you would hear a thud as he fell off his perch, then he would claw his way up the rails again. He didn't have much of a sense of balance, only had one eye, and a wonky leg. Gary had always wanted a parrot, but said he couldn't have one because they live for years and years and if he died who would look after it? Also, parrots tend to latch onto one human but dislike others, so what if the parrot liked Meg but hated him? So instead, they had Bertie the budgie.

Gary was also very understanding with me, but not so obviously as Meg. One day I was particularly depressed about my never having travelled or gone anywhere. He told me that Thinking was the best way to Travel, which I suppose is true, as you only have the happy bits, and not the bad stomachs. He said that like me, he had always been very shy, too shy even to talk to or look at Meg when in the same group at university. She was so cheerful and full of life that he felt he couldn't even say hello to her in case she ignored him. He had sat a few seats away from her on a bus once, and hadn't dared speak, and waited for several stops after his own before getting off, rather than go past her. She had once spoken to him and finished by giving him a big smile, but he thought it was just Postcard Love, and went back into his shell. Of course, she had realised all this, and in the end just came out with it and said to him direct "Well, are we going out or not! We are, so come on." After that, it was plain sailing. Then he really let rip into the Panaceans, and it was so funny that I cheered up completely. Gary described Mrs Barltrop as a Used Prophet. The Daily Scripts she heard from God became "The Daily Mabel." He said a lady called Edna Everage would wonder if the women there had the normal "feminine juices and desires" and I laughed even though I didn't know what it meant. He said I'd not left earlier because I'd got used to an unthinking existence, said I'd stayed because I thought an old raincoat would never let me down. He said who in their right mind would believe all that load of bull (he used a different word but I'm not repeating it). He waved his arms about and paced around as he ranted. When he sat down I thought that he reminded me of a stock cube - small and innocent looking, but full of pent up energy, just waiting to explode.

It got too serious at one point when I said I now realised that I hadn't really lived and began to get weepy, so Meg came and held me close and said " But then again, who does?" She has a good way of putting things into proportion. She told me about something called the Northern Lights, something she'd always wanted to see herself, but never had. I thought that I must have seen them all those years ago looking out to sea that night when I was young and was so happy that they had been in my eyes as well as in my mind. I didn't tell her though. She's such a kind person and she never laughs about the Panaceans, whatever they do. She says she'd love to know what Peter was thinking about as he rode his motorbike. When I'm alone and feeling down, all I want to do is to sit indoors with a strong cup of tea, and watch a black and white film on the television. I did that once when I went into Meg's house as she said I could if I wanted anytime. They leave the door unlocked so I can go in, you see.

And yes, it's funny how all the people I know nowadays are people I like for some reason or another. For a long time I dreaded seeing people (apart from Mrs G of course) as they were all in some way peculiar and put me on edge. And yes, I suppose that's one thing you need to be happy, having people around you that you like. You can only really like the things you really like. And yes, while I'm writing, I think I must make a confession. They once left me to look after Bertie for a few days when they went on a summer holiday. And yes, after three days I suddenly remembered that I'd not gone and given it water and food. And yes, he was in the boiling hot conservatory and was nearly dead. Luckily he bucked up quickly, but I was so relieved and I've never told them.

I've said too much. But perhaps I haven't said enough.

And yes, I also loved the smell of their house. A nice relaxing smell that seemed to put you in a good mood and all light-headed. They said it was the joss sticks, but it wasn't, I'm sure.

I've noticed that Gary, Meg and Eve come round to sit with me a lot more now. Though often it's Lilith not Eve. In fact I'm hardly alone very much at all. Occasionally Gus comes, but all he does is play with his Action Man models. I know it's very nice of them, but it's almost as if they don't trust me to be alone. Meg seemed very relieved when she found me at the cemetery, last week I think it was. I'd gone there to take some flowers, but I got confused and I think someone must have told Meg where I was and she brought me back. I must have got this cold from walking all that way without my overcoat. It was silly of me to do that. I can see it now.

I still like to say "Good Morning" to strangers in the street. Nowadays there are people called 'joggers' who generally ignore you. Worse than anglers they are.

I walked to Albany Road today. I think it might be the last time I'll be able to go there. Everything in the road was quiet and peaceful as if nothing unpleasant ever happened there, and I stopped at all the houses to think about who used to live there. At no 5 Miss Hodgkinson as the Head of House, with Miss Jones, Miss Green, Miss Winna Green, Miss Grey...or was she at no 4? Yes, she was there, with Miss Keeley and Miss Broad. And lately Mr Carew-Hunt, poor deaf and blind man. I know the kind neighbours in the road help out nowadays by cooking food for the ones that are left, and try to look after them. Kind people, just like Meg and Gary. And number 12 itself. There was Mrs Barltrop of course, with Mrs Goodwin, Hilda Green, Miss Hudson as well, and Peter in the attic or the Garden room or somewhere, and perhaps Miss Dilys when she and her mind weren't somewhere else. No 18, such a large house, much too big for just one person, however important he might be! All the gardens had to be planted in exactly the same way, you know. No hollyhocks. One last stroll to the river. Back up Newnham Road, past Glenafron House. They say it was built by a master at the school, and it looked just like Castleside. When he retired, he went to live south of the river, at a place called Paradise. Past The Haven, the conker tree, and a last look at the church. Then as quickly as I can down Castle Road, to home.

I got lost on the way. Someone helped me but I don't know who it was.

I'm getting arthritis in the hands bad now.

Evelyn loved the snowman I made for her you know.

Have I mentioned that I look like Vanessa Redgrave?

Oh yes, I have. And I do.

Speak when you're spoken to. Be seen and not heard. Do as you are told.

Actually, I'm beginning to forget so many things nowadays. I keep losing my keys. I have dozens of them you know. You should never throw keys away. You never know when you might need them.

I think I'll get Lilith to help write down my memories. I trust her. Teenagers take advantage of Kindness from older people, and then ignore you when you need help yourself, but I trust Lilith.

I hear Rita was fined £1 for driving her car at 40 miles an hour in London Road, but she denies it. Oh the horror and shame!

Where did they all go? Where is Evelyn?

Why did I do it? Do I need an alibi?

I've lost my memory, lost my religion, and worst of all, keep losing my favourite pen.

That woman. She was like one of those smiling, slow-moving sloths that Mr Attenborough shows us, but with a dagger in its hand. I think some of us worked at Bletchley Park, you know. Mrs G used to say "Wonderful are the Works of the Wheelbarrow" when I asked her questions she couldn't answer.

My teeth keep on moving about. I wish I could stop them. I'm sure they'll escape one day.

If you see a load of crows, then they're rooks: if you see a rook by itself, then it's a crow. He told me that, and it's true.

So many lost at sea that day.

So many. I think I'd like to learn how to play the spoons. I always stir my tea anticlockwise, but I'm told that's the way Satan does it. Am I bad? The man from the BBC told me to say nothing.

I think there are too many doors in my house.

I'll carry on writing. Lilith tells me I should. I'll use my old typewriter more from now on though. Or I could just dictate to her. Yes, that's what I'll do.

Etholle
Dream - 1988

I had a very strange dream last night. I suppose I must dream as much as anyone, but normally I can't remember it when I wake up. This time it was so strange that I'll write down what I can – just little bits, as it was all so jumbled up that I've probably missed a lot of it anyway:

I'm driving a car along the sea-front of a town that I don't recognise, though in the dream I know where I'm going. I'm trying to find the car park where I've parked the car earlier, which is daft because I'm looking for the car that I'm in! And I can't drive anyway. I drive around, going on pavements and through shops and no one even looks at me let alone tells me off-------Then I'm in Allhallows, and there's a dog on the roof of the pub opposite the Building Society. And on the flat canopy of the Building Society there's a man in a suit who is watering some sunflowers that are growing really high------And there's a group of Hari Krishna people chanting and banging drums and leading a big Ox down the road-----Then I'm running down a road I don't recognise but I'm sure is Albany Road, and I'm going from one house to another, telling myself that there's a better one to go to just around the corner because I'm scared to go into them----Then I'm standing looking up at the Calvary Cross and Mabel is looking down at me with one green eye, still and silent----Then I'm in a forest where no one lives but I come across a hidden garden which is so beautiful that it takes my breath away, and I'm sad because it's a garden in a forest that the world will never see. And there is a great big parrot that flapped his wings at me and says "Hello Eth"-----Then I'm back in the car driving through the forest but somehow it turns into some kind of space rocket and I'm silently gliding past Jupiter and Saturn...Oberon, Miranda and Titania-----Then back into a forest again, where I can hear singing and see a group of performers, led by a lady in black clothes, a hole in her tights, black around her eyes and looking menacing but I know that she's kind really - "I'm just a vision on your TV screen. Just something conjured from a dream"she sings----Then she turns into a white knight and starts to talk backwards and its strange to hear but graceful-----Then a white rabbit comes along and grows bigger and smaller till he goes down a rabbit hole. Then somehow I'm swimming down the hole as well, and there are lots of lights coming towards me and they are all different colours and then there are lots of stars in a very black sky and somehow I feel that I am travelling to a place where I will always be happy---Then I'm in the Garden of Sleep, with poppies and the tower and the fields and the sea and the gulls and I'm singing and dancing--- and singing and dancing.

Phew.

I shew this to Meg, and she laughed and said it sounded like quite a nice trip. It's funny how you forget things. I sometimes wake up with the most brilliant thought or idea but half an hour later I can't remember it. Perhaps people think up wonderful inventions or cures for illnesses in their sleep, but when they wake up they forget it all.

They've changed the label on bottles of Camp Coffee, you know. Aye. Mrs G wouldn't drink any other brand. The Healing never helped her. Never helped me. Only you help me Lilith.

I'd like celery soup for my dinner. I'm suddenly not feeling very well, but I like celery soup.

I used to like singing 'Daisy, Daisy, give me your answer...please'
No, it wasn't 'please.' Celery-lots of people don't like it, though.
It was do. So it's Daily, daily, give me your answer, do.
No, still not right. Daisy, Daisy, sing the praises. No.
Good neighbours, Meg and Gary. And Eve as well. Well, Lilith really. I'm glad they come to see me every day. I stopped them getting Religion, you know. I shew them what's what.
What's Meg written down here in my book? 'Jenny kissed me.'
That's nice. And brought me the celery soup. Thank you. That's a bit better. Did I tell you about the dream?

No, I'll finish now. I've asked Eve to wrap up all my writing and diaries and she can read them when she's older and more knowing.

Or will it be Lilith? They're both nice little mawthers you know. But Lilith is the one.

She'll do something with them, one day.

And yes, I had a kind of Eden.

Gary
Thoughts From The Café

Just a few more loose ends to tie up, while I have a cup of coffee, looking out onto the Garden of Eden. Eat your heart out Costa and Starbucks. The next group will be here soon.

The Panacea Society itself ended in 2012 when the last member, Ruth Klein died, but for years before that plans had been made for the end. The Society was a Charity, but for some time it hadn't really been acting in a way that was in the spirit of the regulations. There was more and more scrutiny from the Inland Revenue and the Charity Commission about what the plans were for the empty Society houses, as the decreasing membership meant some were vacant. The argument that the houses and contents had to be left for the (deceased) occupant to live in again come the Day of Revelation didn't convince the authorities. Houses were modernised and rented out at proper market rates, via an agent, and much of the old furniture and possessions was auctioned off at a sale in the Garden of Eden itself.

The Panacea Charitable Trust took over, and has been responsible for all the charitable work done from 2012. The Trust set up the museum, with free entry, it sponsors academic research into religious studies, and gives a very large amount of money each year to charities and other organisations to do with Poverty and Health. So one way to look at it is that a hundred years ago, the society was set up by a number of very religious well-to-do people with perhaps too much time and money on their hands and with some strange beliefs, but now their memory is being marked by a fascinating museum, facilities for people to study such religious groups, and by giving money away to deserving people for broadly speaking Christian reasons.

So it all worked out well in the end.

Yes, they were strange, but were they mad? Well, they were human beings, and I suppose everyone has their own personal idiosyncrasies, foibles, habits and beliefs, some of which might seem strange to other people. That's one thing that makes an individual an individual. Some of those habits and foibles may be attractive to other people, but some are considered worrying aberrations that hint at the person being so abnormal that they must surely have some kind of mental disorder which should be treated by experts, and might be dangerous to the person and anyone in contact with them. Modern study into this area ends up with a range of terms that only an expert can genuinely understand: Psychosis, Delusion, Schizophrenia, Bipolar Disorder etcetera etcetera etcetera, but the man in the street can at least appreciate that sufferers from these disorders deserve help and understanding. In the case of the Panacea Society members there is much evidence of various disorders, and in truth most of them would have beliefs and habits that undoubtedly could seem 'mad' to 'normal' people .

In several cases it is clear that they were nervous, anxious people who had, and in the Community continued to have, trouble in asserting themselves, preferring the comfort of obeying orders from more authoritative people. They were 'doormats.' Some definitely suffered from Anxiety or panic attacks. Ironically, the more "free-thinking" of the women, who had reacted against their being ignored or suppressed by the male dominated world of the time, in turn had their thoughts suppressed by the rigid rules and authority of the leadership. Most were genuinely searching for "something" in their lives, something to believe in, to cling on to, to make their life meaningful and ultimately to live in the Paradise of Eden. As someone put it: "they were people who fooled themselves into believing something completely ridiculous just because they really wanted it to be so." On the face of it, there's nothing inherently wrong with wanting to live a good life and rid yourself of faults....but there are limits. At a certain point, such good intentions become an obsession, and at that point, the members suffered from Cognitive Dissonance.

Many, perhaps all people suffer from this at some stage in life, but the Panaceans took it to extremes. Put simply, Cognitive Dissonance is a state of mind were you have certain beliefs that are completely contradicted by the facts, yet you convince yourself that you have evidence to show that you are right to hold your own (erroneous) view. The most commonly used example of this is the heavy smoker, who convinces himself that this is good for him as it calms him down and helps him relax, despite the evidence that smoking causes lung cancer. Oh, and anyway, if he gives up, he'll put on lots of weight, so it must be more healthy for him to carry on rather than give up. The smoker holds two contradictory beliefs and can't reconcile them, resulting in unease and discomfort.

Another example is term-time holidays. Headteachers nowadays have to parrot out the mantra that there shalt be no holidays for children in term time, for it is unarguable that every learning day must be sacred, and just one day off will result in the pupil not making the required progress, failing exams and not achieving their potential. The Department for Education says this is so, so it must be so....and parents who think otherwise must be punished by fines, to discourage the others. Yet in reality some such learning days have no scheduled learning, being at the end of term. Or high achieving pupils with otherwise excellent attendance records are forbidden to go on genuinely educational holidays. Any sensible Head with an ounce of Common Sense would know that you just need to apply the flexible rules that once existed and most people would be happy. Perhaps some Heads do have agonies of conscience when refusing requests that are clearly reasonable but are worried about OFSTED inspections, so carry on with the illogicality of following the rules. Good parents will have concerns about the arguments on both sides, and will probably be more uneasy with their eventual decision than the Head.

Or then again, there's the pretence that the ruling monarch is God's chosen person to be the Head of the Church, the Defender of the Faith. In reality, it's all to do with how, hundreds of years ago, a king wanted an excuse to marry a newer version of his current queen and decided the best way would be to set up his own personal Church of England, thus allowing him to do whatever he wanted. Any impartial observer would realise that Henry the Eighth was fooling himself into believing

183

something just for his personal and financial advantage, but ever since there has been the pretence that the monarch is divinely chosen. What made people go along with it in those days, despite their reservations, was that if they voiced their objections they were likely to be sent to their maker pretty pronto, so like some Panaceans, they kept quiet about any reservations they had.

And politicians? Well, just mention "Iraq" and there's a whole casebook for a psychology student studying Cognitive Dissonance.

(Is this getting a bit too deep? Well I don't want your interest to go off the boil, so if you want, feel free to skip ahead three pages or so, starting again at "A group of eccentrics." I'll never know if you do that, and I won't be offended anyway.....but of course if you do, you might miss out on one or two interesting bits).

Panacean beliefs were so clearly unjustified in the face of the evidence that it must have been impossible to reconcile them. Mabel had healing powers, yet the linen did not work in many cases. So they concluded the patient can't have been sincere enough or free of sin, hence the process not working. Mabel herself was ill most of the time. So this must be because she had to suffer for others, just like her brother had. Mabel died, whereas they expected her to live forever. So they scoured the scriptures, and decided that the spirits of dead believers had been flown to the far side of the planet Uranus, and would return in human form come the Day of Revelation. When Kate Firth and Leonard Tucker openly condemned the beliefs and showed how Emily Goodwin had relied on tittle-tattle, not supernatural knowledge, to gain information, some members realised they had been fooling themselves, and left. Others had to decide whether to admit their gullibility or to become even more committed to the beliefs. Once someone makes such a life-changing decision it is well nigh impossible to go back on it at a later date; they had dug their hole, and just kept on digging. Or perhaps they had made their bed and decided to lie on it, and a very cosy bed it was too, with servants around to maintain an easy lifestyle.

Mabel and Dilys, and to a lesser extent Adrian Barltrop suffered from depression. Mabel was put into mental institutions twice in her life, the first time being after she was widowed, with four children, and quite possibly this was something that nowadays could be helped by medication and therapy. A century ago people could be put into such institutions for what seem ridiculous reasons nowadays, such as being an unmarried mother. She heard "voices" for much of her life, but when she was institutionalised the second time she was delusional. She had a message from her late husband in 1916:

"Jesus my Shepherd, Husband, Friend,
My Prophet, Priest and King."

She took this as meaning that Jesus had three incarnations - as Jesus Christ, as her husband, and as a King in the Kingdom to come.

It is quite a common delusion for sufferers to believe that they have supernatural powers or that they are Gods. Generally this is harmless, though ridiculous to the man in the street, but very often such people have a need to tell the world about their very special nature. Mabel probably suffered from Depression, Delusions of Grandeur and Obsessive Compulsion Disorder.

Emily Goodwin was probably more like the commonly accepted idea of a 'looney' than Mabel. She suddenly became the Instrument of the Divine Mother and for many years would snap into the role of a person speaking the words of God the Mother. When in that state, her words were often barely comprehensible, she spoke quickly and moved from one subject to another with no apparent link. She talked in scribble, experiencing reality in a very different way from normal people. This explains her physical battles with demons and devils, with her leaping around (despite her age) and being unaware of it afterwards. At those times an observer might reasonably have thought that she should be put in a straight-jacket. She was like the Wizard of Oz, except that she was never found out.

At those times she probably frightened people around her, and together with her control freakery, made her a figure to be obeyed without question, especially by the largely timid, harmless women of the Community. Or as Tucker put it, the "feeble-minded."

An alternative view is that she might have been a kind and considerate woman, who saw the very real mental sufferings of Mabel, and so pretended to hear voices herself from the Divine Mother, to take the pressure off Mabel, especially at the time of the Edgar Peissart incident. Then, when her predictions somehow came true, she couldn't go back from her new status, and carried on. Very quickly she came to convince herself that her position as Instrument of the Divine Mother was genuine and so there were in effect two parts of the Four-square God in the Community. Two delusional leaders had emerged, making it even more difficult for other members to doubt the validity of the Society's beliefs.

Dilys was the most obvious victim of the way the Community evolved. She was prone to depression most of her life, and treatment in various hospitals here and the Community in France didn't help in the long term. She seems to have been a sensitive person wanting to be close to her mother; in one mass confession, she was one of only four followers who said they had never spoken words against Mabel, but she could have no normal daughter/mother relationship. She went to a normal school, but had to return to a house of middle aged/elderly women who had habits, rules and beliefs that the outside world thought abnormal. Ultimately, she probably found it the easiest option to carry on in this claustrophobic atmosphere and make no attempt to leave. She didn't have the confidence to do so. She moved home several times, never really having normal friendly relationships with others. When she did have occasional happy times with others such as Evelyn Gillett and Olga Hughes she almost immediately turned 180 degrees, and criticised them for being too forward and presumptuous with her. After Emily Goodwin's death the Society clearly wanted Dilys to take over a leading role, as she was her mother's daughter (and hence God's granddaughter) but this was too much for her. After attending a few meetings, she withdrew completely and grew to despise the membership. In the end she died alone. She was buried close to her mother, but in an unmarked grave.

Individually they were mostly eccentric rather than mad, but once they joined into a claustrophobic community, where they were all expected to conform with norms that became more and more extreme they became abnormal. "Group Think" can be dangerous in any area of life, but "Group Belief" was crippling to the normal behaviour of the Community members. As a motorcycle maintenance expert once said, "when a person suffers from a delusion it's called insanity; when many suffer from a delusion it's called religion" (you might add, "Discuss").The harmless enough interest in a Jackdaw that made itself at home in the Garden for some eight years became an example of how extreme little idiosyncrasies could become. He became Sir Jack Daw, and they came to revere him almost as a sacred entity. An elderly spinster might fuss over a small dog that is the centre of her world, but would stop before literally calling it holy; the Panaceans couldn't have such a sense of proportion. In the Community, they were sure they had found what they were looking for because they were told they had found what they were looking for, and anything that conflicted with this was ignored. Zombies. With Stockholm Syndrome, perhaps.

Modern psychiatrists emphase the importance of a patient being open about their feelings and voicing them in confidence, so how was this much different from the Panacean idea of writing down a personal confession, and trying to get rid of faults? The difference is that the psychiatrist uses this to help the patient toward a greater peace of mind, whereas the Panacea system was used to control members.

A group of eccentrics can make up a nice cosy little world, one that you'd like to live in yourself perhaps, like the world of P G Wodehouse characters who are strange but funny, where there is no real evil, just harmless idiosyncrasies. Or like Prince Leonard in his made-up Principality of Hutt River. But the eccentric lifestyle of the Panaceans was different. They made you wary, on edge, not at ease. You'd rather not be there. It carried on till the end. According to the last members No 18 Albany Rd, The Ark, was to be the house prepared for the return of Jesus, and visitors often find this the strangest revelation of all, especially as it is a perfectly normal home. But for years it was just "No 18" and after it was bought, members lived there with no reference to it being a special property. Yes, the Panaceans just made things up as they went along.

The Panaceans did very little harm to people in the outside world, but their way of life did harm to themselves and to each other, especially to their mental state. For the most part, they could be considered at best eccentric and that's how "normal" people saw them in the 1980/90s, small elderly people who were polite enough, but not quite the ticket. Such harmless "eccentrics" still exist. There's Sister Joyce, who still preaches at the top of her voice in the Allhallows area of town, and no one ridicules her or pokes fun at her. Perhaps we're a more tolerant society nowadays. But in the 1920/30s, the Panaceans were less well received. No one wanted them as neighbours if they had the choice. Any prejudice came largely because they were secretive, not because of any evil. They were not mad, nor bad, nor particularly dangerous to know (with a few exceptions perhaps). Some could be cruel to servants, though. Even in the 1970's they told servants off for looking after a neighbour's dog, and even worse inviting non-believers around for tea on Boxing Day. One neighbour wanted to report them to the Police for cruelty but the servant concerned refused, thinking it reasonable for her to be made to wash the curtains from several houses, by hand, in the middle of winter, despite her being in her seventies.

Gary finished his coffee and stood up. He was ready for the next group tour now, had run over in his mind all the details to tell them and the most likely questions they would ask. This was a good place to be in the spring sunshine, half a world away from the imagined Eden of 80 or 90 years before. He could imagine those believers strolling around the garden, almost perfectly happy. Yet nowadays, there were still visitors who found that the place gave them a brief glimpse of Eden. Meg thought there was a Happy Vibe here, and she should know. Only months ago, the place had been packed with hundreds of bright and happy children attending a Book Festival. The building had probably never heard so much laughter and joy since it was built. More recently still, the unique ADP tour finale had brought universal praise from all who attended, together with admiration for those who had created and brought it to Bedford. Today, there had been members of the local Art Society here, getting inspiration from the surroundings to paint their versions of Eden (one lady's painting was definitely the best, and had been earmarked to be put up in the museum entrance). Small groups of two or three were doing what most visitors did; they were standing and staring, wandering and wondering. Several people were playing croquet on the grass, and of course none of them had the faintest idea of what the rules were.

Funny old things, museums. Some people never visit any at all in a whole lifetime, but others can't get enough of them. Regular visitors here felt at home. Doug would have a coffee, reading a book in the Garden every day, happy as Larry. There was the bald-headed man who visited Mabel's house one Saturday every month and said very little, and little did anyone know that once he had been within a single point of being named the Brain of Britain. There were the visitors from far away places, like the lady who had taught Gary the Czech for apple: Yablco (sounded like that, anyway). Was this a weird museum? No, there were far stranger ones around, if you looked for them: the Baked Bean Museum of Excellence, The British Lawnmower Museum, and of course the Cumberland Pencil Museum, so good that Gary had visited it twice. Oh yes, that old string-puller God must have liked the idea of humans having maverick thoughts that could leave one person baffled, but another lost in wonder.

Quite a contrast with that previous career of his, and probably that of most people, 'Travelling in Biscuits' as he put it, working as hard as an Estate Agent's phone on a Monday morning. People had had their own perfect little moments here, experiencing enjoyment that they hadn't imagined beforehand.

But it would soon be time to go home, to look after his other garden.

Lilith
Nothing At The End Of The Rainbow - 2017

Eve sometimes liked to walk to the cemetery in Foster Hill Road, where as Lilith she would wander about remembering times long ago when she and her friends would meet and talk and share their insecurities. A few of them still lived locally but it wasn't the same any more. The odd one might get out his or her black greatcoat and go to the local shopping parade and even pop into the Tesco, but none hung out in the town centre any more. Goths were out, though she'd heard that some Steam Punks ("just Goths who'd discovered the colour Brown") who had moved into the area recently, parading around her old patch. Somehow they were more acceptable than Goths. Things change, though. She'd caught part of a television programme the other day, that had a presenter who definitely shared her own preferred approach to make-up. Goth was becoming more mainstream, or even 'retro.' History might be more interesting from now on. Eve was nearly fifty now, with all the irritating responsibilities that age will soon bring, but when she put on her black lipstick and walked to the other side of town she could get things into perspective, become Lilith again, and remember good times, like the time in Whitby for the Goth Weekend. All the town had been alive with the buzz and the blackness. The normal tourists had hardly blinked to find themselves eating their prize-winning fish and chips next to a bunch of happily morose eccentrics. Less trouble than at a football match they said, but the newspapers didn't report it like that. In her youth she hadn't been perfect of course, but who is? Even David Attenborough or Michael Palin must have their faults if only we knew every detail about them. Yet she was still disappointed when she looked on Facebook and saw that relations or friends she had thought of as "good people" had posted comments she found borderline racist or cruel. You just had to make allowances, to balance disappointment with hope - like the Panaceans had perhaps, years before.

'The cemetery is an old Victorian creation. As in many similar small towns, until early Victorian times most people were buried in churchyards, and as the Church of England had a virtual monopoly of this market, it was a good source of income. But as Industrialisation spread, and the populations of London and the industrial towns of the North increased enormously, these churchyard cemeteries became ...overpopulated. Diseases such as cholera and generally unsanitary conditions meant people died young and the churchyards couldn't cope. There's one case of a churchyard in Islington that had space for 2100 burials, but actually had 20,000 in one year alone in the 1840's. Gradually, towns established municipal cemeteries to cope with the demand in a far better way and Bedford was no exception. James Wyatt, the proprietor of the local newspaper, led a campaign for a purpose-built cemetery, and conveniently he was also the Borough Treasurer, which must have helped. The cemetery was opened in 1855; one of the first burials was of his young son.

There are over 100,000 people buried here although there are now only a few burials each year. Normally this will be someone being buried with their partner, who may have been waiting for them for decades. There are a surprisingly large number of ex Indian Army officers buried here. Apparently an enterprising Headmaster of Bedford School negotiated excellent fees with the Army, so officers moved to Bedford to take advantage, and eventually were buried here.

There is a typical Victorian chapel building, originally with two chapels, one for the Anglicans and one for the non-conformists. Stone monuments lean at drunken angles and some are covered in ivy until volunteers clear away the secrets that might be written on the memorial.

In its way it is a lovely, peaceful place, where you might even hope to find a stone marked "Eleanor Rigby." The Great and the Good of the town are here, mainly in the posh bit, just below the chapel.

Over a hundred members of the Panacea Society are buried in the

191

cemetery, including Mabel and Dilys.'

Lilith sat on a bench next to the chapel, looking down the hill, down past the graves in the posh bit, down over the trees and grass of Bedford Park, and beyond at the town itself. A sunny day, like some she remembered here from 30 years before, and some that were rainy or cold. There were still the big trees that they would gather underneath, and which were still used by the homeless from time to time. Harmless people who still harmed themselves, judging by the syringes left there. She and her group had known the place like the back of their hands – the stones with swastikas on them, the ones with badger setts, the foxes, the stone for the boy who died after cutting his toe with a rusty razor, and the ones that were well looked after. There were the neglected ones, with sad messages on the stones, which made Eve want to put flowers on them to mark the day of birth. Or if she was Lilith, she would do the same on the day of death. Gary had told her about how he had taken Etholle to the cemetery so she could visit the graves of the people she had known from the Society.

Lilith daydreamed. A century before, she decided, another Lilith might have stood in the same spot, watching a funeral hearse make its way through the archway of the Gatehouse, then up the hill, horses struggling to pull the weight along the winding path up to the chapel where it would stop for the passenger to be lifted, shoulder high, and then disappear into the cold sadness of the building and then, perhaps, to a heaven.

Lilith walked down past the wall and meandered around the headstones in the consecrated section. Big headstones, crosses, angels, all sorts of memorials showing how important and rich the people had been, or thought they had been. Even in death it was a case of Keeping Up With The Joneses, to be buried in the best place, with the biggest and most impressive monument. Human Nature doesn't change much over the centuries. She liked to read the messages, the names and the dates on the stones and imagine what the person had been like. "Much Loved Wife of" could mean that really he had been pleased to get rid of the old bat. "Respected Member of the Town Council" might mean

192

the opposite, as they normally aren't. An old soldier's memorial says he fought bravely in several very bloody battles – but who could know this as a fact when he died many years after? Perhaps he had been in the Catering Corps. You could put any sort of untruth on a stone and could get away with it, as the stonemason would be happy as long as he got paid.

Yet some messages were obviously sincere and gave a clear idea of what effect the person's life had had on others. Eve and Lilith both thought the best message was one not on an expensive stone but on a wooden bench that was gradually falling apart:

"A Quiet Kind Man who told a Good Tale, Loved a Joke, and Lit Up our Lives."

She knew of the arcane meanings behind the designs chosen since Victorian times. Carvings could be elaborate, with what might seem unnecessary detail quite apart from the words. The most common choice of monument, after the ubiquitous upright flat slab, was a cross. Usually this was on top of three steps; they represented the three steps to Heaven, Faith, Hope and Charity. The Calvary Cross represented Christian Faith and was a typical Anglican choice. Charity was represented on some stones by a heart. Many stones had elaborate carvings of an anchor, which may incidentally have been the choice of some ancient mariner, but in the secret language of Victorian headstones represented Hope. The odd one had four steps for some reason, perhaps a mistake. Carved Ivy represented Immortality or long Friendship. Lilies were for Remembrance, especially for children. A Pyramid represented Eternity and was thought to prevent the Devil from lying on a grave. Best of all were the carved angels. If pointing upwards they were Agents of God, if pointing downwards they were Guardians of the Dead. They normally had one finger pointing upwards, like a cricket umpire indication the end of an innings, but if there were two fingers it indicated that a clergyman was buried there. One kneeling angel was especially striking, but looked out of place on its grave. Lilith liked things that other people didn't know about, and scoffed when the scariest new monsters on Dr Who, the Weeping

Angels, appeared, as she knew that you'd never find a weeping angel in a cemetery.

She paused by the large stone memorial to a poor young girl murdered in 1885 at a pub called The Ship, in St Cuthbert's St. A large anchor. She was shot while playing tennis by a besotted young suitor, probably deranged after he returned from fighting in Egypt, and had been rejected by the girl. He then killed himself. They were buried a few hours apart with some mourners attending both funerals, and now rest a hundred yards away from each other. In Death he is closer to her than in Life. Lilith and her friends had liked to re-enact the incident (Goths had a reputation to keep up after all) and wondered how many passers-by were aware of the story behind the grave. Most people probably thought it was just someone from a sea-faring family.

Lilith often wondered what the people buried there were really like. She knew of an old Chinese saying that when a person dies, a book is burned. Everyone has a story, a life story, a biography, but only a few of the thousands buried in the cemetery have stories that are in common knowledge. Those life stories may be short, boring, interesting, kind, funny, significant or insignificant, but you can't tell just from looking at a stone or an unmarked piece of grass.

Her father had told her about the Panacea Society members and she had taken it all in. Well, Eve had just listened, but Lilith listened and heard it all, and had always chatted to Etholle as she went about her scatty way talking about this and that. Lilith helped Etholle with her diary and her writing as the old lady's own handwriting became poor. Gary knew so much about them and it was a shock when Lilith found out things that he didn't know about. She'd had that unsettling feeling once before, when a famous person she admired had got easy questions wrong on "Mastermind" and felt she'd been let down by a hero who had turned out to be, er, pretty well thick. And when she found her teachers had gaps in their knowledge, that had been even worse. Gary was honest though, as he admitted that all he knew was how little he knew about anything. She liked him when he was funny, though Eve didn't. Last year, they'd visited a place of Pilgrimage, purely by accident he'd said, and Eve had been embarrassed by him whereas Lilith loved it. They'd walked down the quiet street and he'd asked the elderly and sincere lady in a Charity shop if they could bring in their dog: "He's not been Confirmed, but he's house-trained." Outside a shop he wondered if this was where the pilgrims went for their porn magazines....and then asked the shopkeeper that question. At the gift shop he deliberately scuttled around the aisles of religious books and icons bumping into tall black-robed men who were talking intensely in different languages, and Lilith thought it was just like a scene out of 'Father Ted' and grinned. He could still be like a schoolchild, back from an exciting school trip – just like her. Outside the shop, Eve would look embarrassed and ignore the plump black-robed clerics who wished her Good-Day as they passed by. He came out with a key-ring with St Jude on it."My favourite saint!" he laughed, but meant it. Lilith understood.

Gary knew she noticed when he was a bit angry or upset. She said he went "thin-lipped" but could normally make him laugh. In return, she knew she could always trust him to help her. Once, he had come home to find her crying in a corner, peeling the skin off an orange, saying that she was trying to get it out as it was suffocating. After a while she calmed down, and for the only time in his life he deliberately punched someone, a parasite responsible for ruining lives. For his birthday she would buy him the kind of watch he liked, the cheapest watch she could find (max £6) and have the second hand taken off. "Why be reminded of all those seconds of your life ticking away?" he'd say.

Lilith walked very slowly through the section below the chapel, pausing every so often to stand by memorials to Panacea Society members. In the distance lay Janet Hacking. The lettering on her stone was faded, yet those for her husband were clearer despite him having died years before. And here was Mabel's stern and forthright aunt, Fanny Waldron: "One that feared God and eschewed Evil," and Job should know all about that. Next to her was the first one to die, the ex-suffragette Ellen Oliver whose job had been to be the messenger to God, the eighth angel of Revelation. Lilith gently stroked Ellen's headstone and moved away, her long black coat brushing the grass.

She knew that the apostle Gertrude Searson was buried further up the hill but her stone was gone. Major and Mrs Bean were buried at the side of the chapel, the Pecks were further along the main path, and Mr Boddington was under a tree near the Soldiers' Memorial. His was a very large heavy stone that had fallen down, but Lilith and three friends had managed to turn it upright and one day would set it firm in the ground again. At the Soldiers' Memorial were buried dozens of Panaceans, all together like sheep huddled for protection in rainy weather.

No one had seen any proof of it, but Gary reckoned that sometime during the war an important member, probably Emily Goodwin, had decided to buy plots in this section of the cemetery so that believers could be buried together. She was the first in this section. Many of the important members were here: Peter Rasmussen, Canon Payne, Robert Temple, Muriel and Evelyn Gillett, Donald Ricketts, the Carew-Hunts and Colonel Graham. Strangely, couples weren't necessarily buried together. The Gillett sisters and the Keeleys were together, but both Carew-Hunt brothers were buried apart from their wives. It seemed as if when one died, he or she was just put into the next convenient place with little thought as to who they were with.

Lilith slowly wandered further along towards the edge of the cemetery, past Emily Carew-Hunt (by herself, as if sent to Coventry) and stopped by the grave of Mabel herself. Close by, across a path, was the grave of Dilys, unmarked apart from a stone ornament that Lilith had taken from a rubbish heap and the daffodils, tulips and bluebells that she had planted in the grass a few years before. She felt no aura of holiness or wonder at the grave of God's daughter, just a feeling of sadness that God's granddaughter had been forgotten in such a careless way.

No-one would ever have known that they had all been Panaceans; none of the headstones made any mention of the Society. Most messages were mundane though sincere. Lilith had always been puzzled by this, but could only put it down to the fact that the memorials were probably chosen by sons or daughters who were not themselves members.

Mostly, they wished for a "Better Resurrection." The words chosen for Emily Goodwin's grave were from Solomon, a strange choice. Gary and Meg had sent the young Eve to Sunday School, and she had loved the words of that book of the Bible, but later on Lilith realised that the words were full of smut, double meanings, suggestive. It was all about sex, something that Emily Goodwin probably wasn't too keen to talk about. Mabel's grave was the most mysterious, though. It had the initials, M.B, but not her name, and "O S-J".

Gary told her it meant that here was buried Octavia the prophet, who was also Shiloh-Jerusalem. The Panaceans emphasised the importance of the feminine in their beliefs. Mabel was the *female* Messiah Shiloh. They took from previous prophets of the Visitation, John Wroe and James Jezreel, the belief that the female 'Immortal Spirit of God' was 'Jerusalem.' St Paul had referred to 'Jerusalem above' being the 'mother of us all.' Rachel Fox wrote 'The Sufferings and Acts of Shiloh-Jerusalem' which was a conscious merging of the concepts of a female Prophet/Daughter of God/Immortal Mother Spirit of God. They had complicated beliefs, interpreting the Bible in ways to fit in with the theological world picture they found comfortable. The words chosen for Mabel's grave were therefore very carefully chosen. Believers would easily recognise that this was the grave of the person who was their Salvation; *she* was the Resurrection and the Life.

Lilith slouched towards the chapel again, occasionally looking back. A couple walked past Mabel's grave, unconcerned that they had just been close to God's daughter. They had somewhere to get to, and walked calmly on.

Eve had been the cleverest of the clever, the brightest of the bright, with an imagination as big as a Klingon Battle-cruiser, or so Gary said. Yet at university Lilith just couldn't be bothered, and now had a series of non-jobs that just paid the bills. But secretly Gary knew that there was a spark that would reappear someday. She would be the reverse of Peter Cook.

She stopped, and decided to go to an open grassed section where there were no monuments. Etholle had been buried here, but she couldn't remember the exact spot so she sat on an anonymous piece of grass to think about her family's former neighbour. From the deep pocket of her coat she took a blue marbelette diary and thumbed through it, occasionally making a face of disapproval. Much of what was written was a complete sham, giving an impression of a life and a truth far different from what she herself remembered. Yes, Etholle had been a harmless and innocent old lady, but she told lies. She was a fantasist. As far as Lilith was concerned, most of what people thought about Etholle was wrong.

Lilith got up, and Eve walked out into Foster Hill Road, back to see her mother and father. She went to see them every day, religiously. Meg didn't get out much now and rarely smiled as she used to.

Eve's brother had gone – he never even made it to his twenties.

Home with the Clancys-2017

Another day's volunteering over, Gary was ready to go home. Depending on his mood, perhaps he might go along Castle Road where he was bound to bump into someone he knew and get a cheery wave from Rogan's Book Shop.Then he'd look at his favourite piece of topiary, just past the roundabout. Someone had made a hedge in their front garden into the shape of a large unicorn, with a Rupert the Bear on top of it. Twenty years of careful cutting apparently. Or on the other hand, perhaps he'd take the longer route via the Embankment, which was better for seeing something unusual or for daydreaming. He decided on the more sociable route, and turned right, past The Haven, glanced at the church in the middle of the road, then along to the junction with Albany Road. Past number 18, The Ark, the house where some later believers believed they would house Jesus when he returned (conveniently situated near a used car lot, and opposite the Panacea Allotments). A prime location for housing, the Society had turned down offers to sell the allotments and instead it had stayed as a gift for townspeople to enjoy. They weren't "moneygrabbers"after all. He did wonder though whether there had been any clause in the rental agreement stating that if Jesus did return he would be legally entitled to any veg being grown there.

Anyway, as he was clearly starting to daydream, he changed his mind and his route, and walked down Albany Road to the Embankment. He didn't often walk by these terraced houses, in the road that so many of the Panaceans had colonized, where they had deliberately chosen to eat, sleep, and be, just a few yards away from their Eden. Several of these houses were still rented out, to people who were in their way very proud to live in houses once occupied by those minor celebrities. The days were long gone when the road was full of a particular kind of Hope, with groups of quiet harmless people buzzing like bees around their hive and their queen and the distant murmur of their prayers, but he felt it did still have something of an aura about it. It was a comfortable road, just as the Panacea Garden was a comfortable place to sit and think. There was no worry, no unnecessary pressures, no phobias, but a feeling of optimism, where the biggest concern was the danger of ladybirds damaging the exhibits in the museum. Only the best of people can produce an environment where people genuinely look forward to a workplace, and normally they have no idea of how they do it.

As he turned along the Embankment, along the edge of the river, he made a mental list of a few things that he could amuse Eve with later on, by him having one of his planned unplanned rants, pretending to be a Grumpy Old Man:

Barn Conversions
Gap Years
Designer Labels
Misused Hooray Words like Artisan
Safe Spaces
Unpaid Internships
Micro-Management
Button-holes

That would do for the moment. He could think of much more, but knew he could never 'out Jimmy' the real Uncle Jimmy, one of his favourite awful comedy characters, whose rants he could quote word for word. He stopped, and as there was no-one in hearing distance, pretended to complain loudly to the river about:

"Communists, Maoists, Trotskyists, neo-Trotskyists, crypto-Trotskyists, union leaders, Communist union leaders, atheists, agnostics, long-haired weirdos, short-haired weirdos, vandals, hooligans, football supporters, namby-pamby probation officers, Wedgwood-Benn, keg bitter, punk rock, glue-sniffers, Clive Jenkins, Roy Jenkins, Up Jenkins, up everybody's."

Once, someone had heard him shout his favourite lines, and crossed the road to get away from such an obvious looney. But Gary knew he was just enjoying himself, so he cared bugger all for what strangers thought of him. He could well appreciate how irritated Mabel might have been by certain little things, such as people who ate noisily, spoke loudly or out of turn or dressed improperly and all the rest of the things she banned from her Eden. Perhaps she hadn't been all that unreasonable.

Satisfied, he carried on past the flower gardens, past the Embankment Hotel (which once had an eccentric neighbour, who used to keep a donkey in his garden), past the memorial, past Rothsay Road, and then crossed into Russell Park where his children had had so much fun years before. He liked playing little tricks. Last April, he'd made up a note that he'd put under the Jerusalem window in the chapel, similar to the ones that members had written in their time, donkey's years ago:

'To The Great Divine Mother Jerusalem

May I humbly ask for Thine over-ruling and guidance on the matter of the European Union Referendum. I am confused by the statements made by The Lord's subjects on this earth, and beg you through your Divine Grace, to give a sign as to how you would wish me to act. I know that your daughter Octavia only allowed voting in exceptional circumstances, and wish to know whether you consider this event to be of any importance.'

No-one had said anything about it, but it wasn't there when he went back to get it at midday.

He went up Denmark Street (Rock and chips tonight perhaps?) back onto Castle Road and then home to where Meg would be waiting. Eve would pop in tonight as well, as she always did. He was proud of the way she had turned out, perhaps due to his wise parenting? No, more likely it was just an accident of birth.

Meg's only contribution to the evening was to tell Eve that on that day's 'Pointless' a contestant in her fifties said she was a member of a "Goth only" branch of the W.I. Gary said that a visitor that day had told him he was writing a novel about a pub darts team whose members only met so that they could discuss survival plans for the upcoming Zombie Apocalypse. Lilith's interest perked up at the thought of those two examples of the quirkiness she liked, but she didn't stay long, as she was in a thoughtful rather than a talkative mood. She left her father pottering around doing not very much and her mother stroking the cat, blankly, and saying something about having seen helicopters on the walls of Troy. They did talk about a television adaptation of a book they had read, and how the actors chosen were nothing like the characters they imagined just from reading the book itself. This lead on to him thinking about actors who might be most similar to the Faces who lived in the Eden a few hundred yards away, once upon a time. Olivia Colman as Mabel, definitely. Glenda Jackson as Emily Goodwin, Sheridan Smith as Dilys, Steve Pemberton as Piessart, Jessica Raine as Evelyn, that bloke from "Wolf Hall" as Rasmussen. Or Keeley Hawes as Dilys, or Evelyn- impossible to get it all right, but easy to get it wrong.

Lilith walked the few steps to her home, settled down in a large chair and again thought about Etholle, the real Etholle rather than the one she had made herself out to be.

The old woman had pestered away so much over the years that her parents felt guilty if they didn't let her into their home. She would stand looking over into their back garden, silent and unmoving. She pretended to be ill so Meg would come round and tidy her house, do her shopping and be at her beck and call. Meg was so soft hearted that she gave her a key "if you ever need it" but never got it back. In return, she would come back to a house where Etholle had made herself at home, drinking tea and watching the television. "I'm just babysitting" she would say, even if it was in school hours. CDs went missing, LPs were jumbled up and later found in Etholle's house, laid out on the floor so she could see all the designs on the covers. She had let their budgie out and replaced him with a ball of wool and was sure no-one would notice. When she was in the Clancys' kitchen she would secretly set the toaster at the highest level, so that it burnt black and they always had to reset it. One year she knocked on every door in the road, telling strangers that she had no idea who the next Archbishop of Canterbury was going to be. She wandered about the town singing hymns, but with obscene words. She harassed the elderly Panacea

Society members in the street, claiming that she was their leader. She rang the BBC eighteen times in one day to complain about the number of times they played Terry Wogan's 'Floral Dance' on the radio. She tried to set up a 'Knit and Pray' society with the down-and-outs in Pigeon Square. She followed Lilith and her friends around the streets, and wore black lipstick. She had become quite deaf, so every unbalanced comment she made was heard by everyone nearby as she shouted. Children knew her as 'old screw loose Eth.'

Meg always helped her, but it was normally Gary who had to find her when she went missing. Often, she would make an expedition to the cemetery on the other side of town, in her bedclothes, to visit her friends. She knew where they all were, and at one point dug small holes in some graves and left messages she had written. In the end Gary had had enough but Meg insisted on carrying on, as this was just an unfortunate old lady who was losing her memory.

Etholle had died quite suddenly, a few days after rummaging through Meg's "medicine cabinet." Lilith had been helping her in the last few days, sorting her things out such as they were. Etholle had an old tin chest with her "treasures" in it, placed on a shelf that was high up and always cluttered. "The shelf is full, so that no-one can ever say I'll be left on the shelf" was Etholle's reasoning. Etholle herself couldn't reach it in her last few years, though Lilith knew all about it. Lilith had found an old photo of a young man with an old skool moustache, with faded unclear writing on the back, torn into several pieces. There was an old remembrance poppy, which she had kept in her handbag all year round "in case of an emergency." There was an old newspaper cutting of a group of people gathered together on a beach. There were some childish drawings, one of a girl standing on a large circle with outlines of the continents, and underneath were the words "I'm looking over the edge!" Another was of 'Alice, when she's ten feet tall.'

There was the 1885 volume of " The Sunday at Home. The Family Book for Sabbath Reading." It was well-thumbed, and page 557 had been turned down as if for quick reference.

There was an old autograph book, with messages written probably by young adults to each other when they went their different ways at the end of their studying days. There was the usual "By hook or by crook, I'll be last in this book" followed by someone else writing below it "Not so fast. I'm last." But Lilith's favourite was one that made her think about the message on Ellen Oliver's grave.
It was a kind of parody of the Book of Revelation:

"The lightning flashed, the thunder roared,
and all the world was shaken.
The little pigs curled up their tails,
and ran to save their bacon."

Lilith hadn't told anyone about the things she found in the box, apart from showing her parents the old Bible that Etholle had long ago thrown into it. She didn't tell anyone about the pages of signatures reading "Delyth Gwynne" and "Etholle Andrews" that someone had clearly been practising time and time again till they got it right. Etholle, Mrs Gwynne's lifelong servant, had somehow inherited her house after her death, and had simply stayed there with no-one ever questioning what had happened. Then, after Etholle's death, the property had become empty and one Spring day, Lilith made the house her own. No-one could find any record that Etholle had ever existed, as there was no birth registered. No-one in authority seemed bothered to find out who owned the property. Perhaps there had been a mistake made by a solicitor at some point, or Etholle had taken the property fraudulently-identification procedures were less strict in the 1930's - or perhaps records were lost in the war. Nobody knew where Etholle got the money to live on after Mrs G died. In any event, Eve moved in to look after it, but straight away Lilith took what she called squatter's rights and it became her own home.

No one ever queried what had happened, nor did anyone realise that some of Etholle's handwritten memories from over the years had been carefully altered. Some pages had been torn out, and whole paragraphs changed.Well, after all, something typed could have been written by anyone at any time, and unlike fingerprints, everyone's handwriting changes over the course of 70 years, doesn't it.

The End

Well, I've almost finished writing something inspired by the Panacea Society, and the effects it might have had on people over a period of 80 years or so.

Did the last bit surprise you then?

All along, you've liked Eth, and then in the space of a couple of paragraphs, I've turned everything on its head. You liked her, the poor innocent orphan, smiled at her little idiosyncrasies, wanted her to have a real friend in Evelyn. You sympathised with her in her simplicity, really felt for her as she stood outside the Reading Rooms, alone, listening to the happiness dancing inside. She was a nice dotty old lady who had been dealt a life without much love, who was getting old and forgetting things, just as any elderly relation you or I might have will perhaps go the same way. You almost wished she could die at the end of her Dream, "I'm in the Garden of Sleep, with poppies and the tower and the fields and the sea and the gulls and I'm singing and dancing....and singing and dancing." She was happy there. But she lived on for a while, and you were on her side. Me as well!

Then suddenly she's become a liar, constantly interfering with the lives of the neighbours, becoming a burden to them because of their kindness and understanding. She is a pest. You can't believe anything she said or wrote. So who to believe?

Well, it was Lilith who made the revelation about Etholle. According to fable, a Lilith was Adam's first wife. A bad 'un she was. Lilith the 'Seducer of Men,' Lilith the 'Baby Strangler.' Oh yes, a bad 'un. Surely you mustn't believe the word of anyone with a name like that, right? You mustn't give her the benefit of doubt, just as you have to be scared of Goths even if they kindly help an old lady called Etholle when she falls over. That fooled you as well, didn't it.

So, who to believe?

I like Eth. And Mrs G. And bits of the others. I have to say that, because some of the things I've made them do or say are things that have been done or said by people I've known, or even by me. Yes, I once left a budgie in a hot conservatory and forgot to give it water for two days (it survived) and my mother did Etholle's trick of unknowingly singing hymns to a dying patient in hospital (her relations did thank my mother).

I hope you'll see that I've tried to give an affectionate picture of Etholle, and of the Panaceans generally. People do have the idea that the Panaceans looked like Etholle, small, old fashioned, reclusive and distant. But you shouldn't judge a book by the cover should you? That little old lady who rises early every day, that you see wandering around your street, who always says "Good Morning" to anglers, joggers and mobile phone zombies alike might not be what you think. She could be a spy or a mass murderer or a messiah. You can imagine her as almost anything, as writers would.

In their different ways, I've made Etholle and Mrs Fox, Eve and Lilith, Meg and Gary, Mabel and Mrs G, and Evelyn and Dilys give an idea of what the Panaceans' Eden of a hundred years ago might have been like. I'm glad you've stayed the distance, read it all, and I hope you've enjoyed it, a "heterogeneous congeries of amalgamated matters." I'm pleased with several sections and memorable phrases, though in places I'm not sure whether I thought them up myself or remembered something I read years ago. And did you spot many of the clever and not so clever references to songs, poems and so on? Only two in this last chapter I think. Maya Angelou is one of them.

Perhaps you'll now agree with the comments in the museum visitors' book, that they were fascinating, enigmatic and a bit weird. Like all humans they had flaws, but they were also sincere and in some ways admirable. They did little harm. They were as enigmatic as a solitary Boab tree, as unlikely as a stramatolite, but chained themselves to a world that was nearly extinct. And they left a few unanswered questions and loose ends, just like this book really. And by the way, who do *you* think wrote Etholle's memoirs? And what happened to Gus? Go on...I've left a few clues for you to work things out.

And another thing: if you've found the idea of the Panacea Society interesting, then follow the advice of the guide on the John Bunyan Boat (that's the one where you met my granddaughters Poppy and Tula at the start of the book).

Visit the museum, or go to www.panaceatrust.org.

That'll do then.Apart from.....let's have another, closer look at 16th October 1934.....

Looking Through Dilys Barltrop's Eyes- October 1934

Everything in the room was still. No noise. Quiet as the grave, well, almost. The whole house was going through the motions of being busy as usual, but some downstairs had edginess in all they did. Whispered conversations in corners. Worried looks. Frowns. Suppressed tears. A handkerchief, quickly taken out to blow a nose that didn't need to be blown or wiped, then slowly put back into the sleeve of a cardigan, worn daily in this place dedicated to the work of the one upstairs who was their whole world, but not long for it. Only a few knew the truth of what was happening. In the Sitting Room two figures sat or occasionally paced about, sometimes going to a Bible on the table, flicked through the pages hopefully, anxiously, looked up as if about to pronounce some wisdom, then sat down again, crestfallen and beaten. Silence again.

Upstairs, the small bedroom for the servant was empty. So was the large room at the front, Mrs Goodwin's room, though it always seemed that someone was there. You always felt that she was watching; she was everywhere. At the back of the house, Dilys lay on her bed, staring at the ceiling, door shut. The upper room, where once the devotions had been carried out, was empty, but open for the despondent to sit, sharing it with Angst instead of the Hwyl of happier times. In the attic, Peter stared out of the small window, looking to the South, distraught, as he was one who knew what was happening in the room below.

In Mabel's bedroom, nothing moved, but from the mantelpiece Dilys' eyes looked out at her mother's final domain. This was the centre of the world, the Royal Domain, Eden. The whole universe was here. But now, God's daughter was laying motionless in a bed, in a small room, in a small town, dying. The dying person's world is small, limited, one of frustration and contempt.

Dilys' flat, emotionless eyes looked out of the window. In the bed, Mabel lay still and uncomfortable. This must be near the end. Years and months of depression and then pain in the arms, the legs, rheumatism, shingles, ears. All nerves crying out. Giddy sensations. Can't get out of bed. People come into the room. Hilda, Peter, little flower Dilys, Emily. A doctor – what can he do that I can't?

Can see to the opposite corner of the room, the wardrobe, the chairs in the middle of the room, but things are getting cloudy. Eyes watering. Someone has lit the fire, but I don't remember seeing them. The washstand with marble top, so far away now. Can turn head to the right and can just see the calendar. Hilda changes it every day. 15Th it says. Always so efficient, she never forgets what has to be done.

On the mantelpiece, Dilys' emotionless eyes stared out of the window.

Are you feeling better yes I'm quite comfortable I'm a bit cold though hold my hand please not too tight that would never do but it helps please hold me. Eyes closing quite restful now where have they gone who was that? Awake again. Ah, can see Helen Shepstone in the distance. Helen Shepstone Helen Exeter looking at me next to the mirror but I can't see myself in it. Pictures on the wall dear Dilys and Lord Jesus with the flock of lambs gathering his flock I gathered my flock to be his flock but he will come soon I will go in the garden walk in the garden in Eden my Eden we will walk he will call me his sister his wife we will all walk in the garden all of us as promised here in Bedford in Eden always six o'clock always teatime forever and ever ....Colder now. Has someone been in here the fire is warmer now but I can't see it at all I think someone is here with me ...someone is here but I can't see them .. it must be Jesus my brother my husband he is here I lift my hand to him he holds it . ..getting lighter again but I can't move I can't move my eyes ...am I dying now or am I alive I must be but how hard is it to die what do I have to do?

Dying should be easy; you just go to sleep, and then forget to wake up again.

The household was quiet. They thought she must be sleeping,

but at 11.30 Peter went into the room and found her apparently in a coma. The doctor came and gave an injection into her heart, but she died that day. That afternoon, after hours of wondering what to do, they changed the clothes and bed linen to make her clean and right, ready for resurrection. Only a few were told. And then they waited. Nothing happened, so they lit the fire to keep her warm. They gave her hot water bottles, they gave her brandy, they gave her the water. Nothing happened. No resurrection. No signs. She no longer looked like their beloved Octavia Their Only Hope. But surely that didn't matter, because when she arose, she would begin Life all over again.

17th – nothing.
18th – nothing .
19th despite the vigils, the prayers, the reading of the scripts and the gospels and the prophets, nothing.

They called the undertaker to arrange the funeral, and decided how to tell the flock about what had happened, and what was to happen.
Across the campus, work carried on as usual, though all was subdued. Dilys' eyes stared out of the window, looking at the Garden of Eden.
   Yes, go and order these flowers will you. And if Mr Walden asks whose funeral it is, do not reply, or just say "Oh I don't think you would know the name" but better still, say nothing.

There's more to this history than meets the eye. If you want an explanation for some of the many little puzzles and hidden messages (who is the girl in this photo? for example) please request your "A level study cheat notes" from adiebean@hotmail.com.

If you want a concise, understandable account of The Panacea Society, written in a conversational style - this is it:

Here is Everything You Ever Wanted To Know About The Panacea Society, a fascinating ornament of Twentieth Century England.

It is also a biography of Etholle, a fictional character who gets involved in the strange goings-on of the group.

An occasional participant in Panacea life, she sees the Northern Lights, meets The Daughter of God, loves country dancing, sees the Jarrow Marchers, and writes her life's story.......

Or does she?

There are references (real and imagined) to people and events in the history of Bedford.

And just for fun, there are hidden quotes and references to songs, poems and books which you might find hard, or easy, to spot.

This book is written by a volunteer at the Panacea Museum. The sale proceeds will be given to charities, including those concerned with mental illnesses.